Handy Man's
Concrete
and
Masonry
Handbook

by **R. J. DeCristoforo**

New York

Fourth Printing, 1973

Published by ARCO PUBLISHING COMPANY, Inc.
219 Park Avenue South, New York, N.Y. 10003

Copyright MCMLX by Fawcett Publications, Inc.

Library of Congress Catalog Card Number: 60-13052
ISBN 0-668-00729-X
Printed in the United States of America

The editors thank the following organizations for their
photographs and cooperation: Besser Co., Filon Plastics
Corp., Kraftile Co., Louisville Cement Co., Permanente
Cement Co., Portland Cement Assoc., Smooth-On Mfg. Co.,
Title Council of America, Inc., and U. S. Gypsum Co.

CONTENTS

Concrete Facts

Making good concrete is like baking a cake—have a good recipe, follow directions

A wheelbarrow can be used to mix small amounts of concrete. Clean barrow thoroughly after using it.

Bottomless box, sized to hold 1 cubic ft., is good measuring device when hand-mixing ingredients.

Cement, sand, gravel are mixed so no streaks of brown or gray show; add water in formed hole.

THINK of concrete as being an artificial stone; its manufacture the result of careful mixing of properly proportioned ingredients. It's almost like making a cake. If you have the correct recipe and follow the directions you automatically create a successful product.

There are many reasons that make concrete one of the most widely used construction materials. These factors explain its wide use in industry and the same reasons apply to you as a homeowner interested in property improvements at minimum cost. When freshly mixed, concrete can be molded into virtually any shape, stationary or portable. If portable relative to a mass of concrete sounds puzzling, think of the many decorative outdoor projects that are evident today: beautiful bowls to hold colored pebbles and water, planters, patio bench tops and table tops, small running-water pools and so on.

Concrete is strong and durable and improvements made with it take much abuse, last indefinitely and require a minimum of maintenance. Cost of concrete projects is comparatively low and the speed with which it can be mixed, poured and used is a real asset in terms of seeing your handiwork materialize quickly.

Different effects are easily achieved and here you can be imaginative so that even concrete work can have an individual and creative flair. You're not limited to the standard wood float or steel trowel surface finishes. Just "sweeping" it with a broom (after it has set sufficiently) can produce a striated surface or one with attractive swirls. Washing it with a hose exposes some of the larger aggregates which are part of the basic concrete formula. The roughness of the surface under this treatment can be relative to the amount of set-time the concrete has had and the pressure of the water coming from the hose.

You can inset attractive stones or pebbles, even wood blocks. You can make mosaics. You can have a stretch of paving which will be a conversation piece in your garden or you can have a patio so smooth it makes a good dance floor. All these things and much more are possible if you fully exploit what is really a wonderous and modern material.

Can You Do It?

Concrete work is not difficult but any good size project requires some labor. The ingredients are not lightweight, but the secret is to tackle just the amount you can handle in the time available. Even a good size patio can be constructed piecemeal if you "grid" the design so the total is composed of many areas three or four feet square. You can easily complete several of these areas in a few hours. In this way you can pace yourself. Savings are substantial. A gridded patio, worth $300 professionally done, can be yours for less than half that if you do all the labor yourself. Even if you don't care to tackle the heavy end of the work, you can save a lot by doing the preliminary jobs such as paving, leveling and laying the forms and then contracting for the cement work.

Concrete Ingredients

Portland cement, sand, gravel or crushed

Mix carefully so water doesn't run off. Mix thoroughly so gravel is coated with cement-sand paste.

Stiff surface gotten by flattening pile with shovel means the mix is good; use mix within half-hour.

stone and water are used to make concrete. The first three materials you buy from a local supply house. The water you get from your own drinking supply, and it should be that kind of water—fit enough to drink.

When these ingredients are mixed together in proper proportion, the cement and the water form a paste which thoroughly coats all the aggregates and, after hardening, bonds them together into the artificial stone we call concrete. A carefully measured amount of water assures a water-cement paste with maximum strength. You can get away with slight variations in the amount of aggregates suggested for a given mix without reducing the strength of the final product, but good results are very much dependent on exact water measurements relative to the amount of cement used. Extra water produces a thin, weak bonding paste and, although your project may look okay to begin with, you will find that it is actually a weak and less durable product.

Actually, too little water is much better than too much, so long as you get a workable, plastic mixture. Unless you measure exactly with aggregates that are perfectly dry, a good procedure after all the aggregates and the cement have been thoroughly dry-mixed is to add a small amount of water at a time, mixing as you go until the mass is pliable and you can compact some of it in your hand and have it stand without crumbling.

Facts About Aggregates

Aggregates are either "fine" or "coarse." Sand, broken down slag, gravel, pebbles, crushed stone—all of these are aggregates.

The difference between fine and coarse aggregates is determined by size. "Fine" means those that range from sand grains to particles that will pass through a $\frac{1}{4}$" mesh screen. Coarse particles range from the maximum in the "fine" category to pieces that are an inch and a half in diameter and even larger. This doesn't mean that all pieces in a particular aggregate will be exactly the same size. It does establish the minimum and maximum sizes; pieces in a batch will range between.

There is a simple reason for this. If all the pieces were large the concrete mix would be full of holes like a box filled with basketballs. If, on the other hand, the box was filled with marbles, golf balls and baseballs in addition to the basketballs, the spaces between the large balls would

WOOD FLOATS YOU CAN MAKE

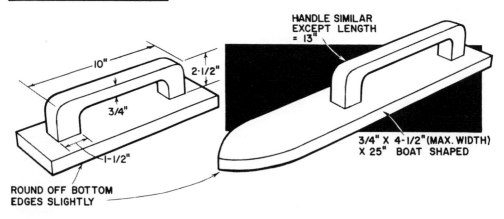

10"
2-1/2"
3/4"
1-1/2"

HANDLE SIMILAR EXCEPT LENGTH = 13"

3/4" X 4-1/2"(MAX. WIDTH) X 25" BOAT SHAPED

ROUND OFF BOTTOM EDGES SLIGHTLY

CUBIC FOOT BOTTOMLESS MEASURING BOX

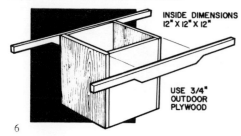

INSIDE DIMENSIONS 12" X 12" X 12"

USE 3/4" OUTDOOR PLYWOOD

STRIKE BOARDS

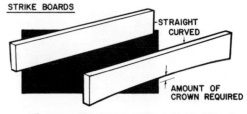

STRAIGHT
CURVED

AMOUNT OF CROWN REQUIRED

USE 3/4" STOCK FOR SHORT SPAN — GO TO 2X4 OR 2X6 FOR LONG BOARDS

be filled by the smaller. That's why aggregates, after being taken from the natural source of supply, are screened, graded and mixed in proper proportion to include enough pieces of each size. The finer particles eliminate voids between large pieces and result in good use of cement paste in bonding all size particles together in a strong and durable structure.

Usually the job you're doing will determine the best size aggregate to use. Thick construction like foundation walls and footings will take the larger size aggregates. Thinner projects like some slabs, flagstones and stepping stones will take smaller ones. A good rule for thinner projects is to use aggregates in which particles are never more than one third the thickness of the finished project.

Buying Materials

You can choose one of several ways to secure materials. Buy all the ingredients separately and make your own mixes. This is a good idea when you have several different projects to do that may require different proportions. Buy a concrete mix (sand and gravel already thoroughly mixed) so all you have to do is add the correct amount of cement and water. Or

you can buy all the ingredients already mixed, including the water, delivered to your door in a special truck all ready to pour. You can even buy a small sack of concrete mix or mortar mix that includes everything but the water. The latter is ideal for small jobs and repair work.

Secrets of Mixing

Proportions for a good, workable mix that is adequate for most home improvement jobs can be based on the following:

One cubic foot portland cement (1 sack)

Two and one-fourth cubic feet of sand

Three cubic feet of gravel or crushed stone

Five gallons of water

These amounts when thoroughly mixed could be shoveled into a pile that has enough adhesion even when wet to hold together without spreading. Any mix you make should be able to stand without spreading flat or being slushy. Even pieces of aggregate which are on the surface of the mix will stay in place and have a full coating of the water-cement paste. It is obvious that this is due not only to correct proportions but to thorough mixing. If water runs off, you've used too much. A further test of

If truck can get to the site, it deposits ready-to-finish concrete where you want it. Be ready, have help.

Use a shovel to get the concrete into all corners. It's a good idea to wear a pair of old overshoes so you can get around easily.

Use a shovel vertically to work concrete, especially against the forms. On deep pours, use a 2x4 for this.

a good batch of concrete is to smooth the top of the pile with a shovel or with a trowel to determine if a good finish can be produced without excessive surface water.

One consideration that will affect the amount of water to use is the moisture content of the "dry" materials. Sand, for example, can hold considerable moisture even though the surface of the pile appears dry. So it's a good idea to use *less* water than the recipe calls for—you can always add more if needed. A simple way to check the sand is to compress a handful of it and then open your fingers. If the sand falls easily between your fingers you can be pretty sure it's dry. If it holds the compressed shape it has enough water in it to affect the mixture proportions.

Consider your first mix as sort of a trial, using less water than necessary and noting the amounts used. Make the pile test and when the mix is right, use the same amount of water for following batches. Remember the amount of water in relation to cement should remain constant. The workability of the mix can be controlled by greater or lesser amounts of the sand and gravel. Use less of these in a trial batch of concrete if it's too stiff to work. If the mix is too wet, add some sand and gravel

but try to keep the proportions of two and one fourth parts sand to three parts gravel constant in the batch unless you require a finer, smooth mix, in which case you can decrease the amount of gravel and replace it with sand.

Have a bucket handy so you can measure amounts exactly. A ten-gallon pail, marked off to indicate quarts and gallons can be used for water. For the other materials you can make a bottomless box with 12"x12"x12" inside dimensions. This will measure one cubic foot of dry materials. Remember too, that a standard sack of cement contains one cubic foot (94 lbs.).

Unless you have a very large area to pour in one uninterrupted slab, it's perfectly feasible to attempt mixing your concrete by hand. It's probably the toughest part of the job but only because it requires some work. You can make a mixing trough or use a wheelbarrow depending on how much you need. Whichever the case, the surface on which you mix should be smooth and waterproof. You don't want water running off carrying away precious cement with it. A large sheet of waterproof plywood will do. If you want to make a permanent mixing trough, add 2'x6' or 2'x8' sides and ends to the platform to make a large shallow box. For occasional

amount of concrete to make, think about renting a small, powered mixer. You can rent one in a half-bag (cement) size which you can work with easily and which produces a large enough batch of concrete in a fast enough time to satisfy anyone. Some of these are powered electrically. Still others have a hand crank and require considerable labor but are still easier than hand shoveling.

Before renting one of these, be sure that you are completely prepared to fully exploit the rental time you are paying for. All materials should be on hand. Forms should be in, grading done and the job thought out and planned.

Use of materials is the same as in hand mixing. Put the dry materials in first and let the drum revolve for good mixing. Then add the water and let the machine run for several minutes or until examination reveals that all the aggregates are coated. The load in the drum is then dumped into a wheelbarrow and carted to the site for pouring into the forms. Of course you should set both materials and machines as close to the site as possible to avoid unnecessary labor. If the project permits, it might be possible to dump the contents of the drum directly into the forms themselves.

How To Handle Ready-Mix Concrete

Ready-mix means that a truck will come to your door with cubic yards of wet, ready-to-pour concrete and expect to spend a minimum of time unloading. This doesn't mean they'll dump it in a pile and go on their way. It does mean that you should be all ready to receive them with adequate help to handle the amount of concrete you've ordered. Be sure that the truck can get to the building site, otherwise you'll have to cart it from truck to site in a wheelbarrow. Check beforehand to see if your driveway will support the truck's weight. It might be possible to drive over a lawn if you plank it with 2'x12's and if the lawn is dry.

A ready-mix truck can empty a number of cubic yards of concrete in fairly short order so be sure you can handle it. Once you start this job, you've got to see it through to the end. Have a buddy or two around to lend a hand and be completely prepared as far as job planning is concerned. Know exactly where and how you want the cement dumped and be sure the material will arrive sufficiently early in the day to allow you enough time to go through all the necessary finishing operations. This is important.

jobs you could mix right on a smooth pavement or driveway.

Shovel the dry ingredients onto your mixing platform (or use the bottomless cubic box) and mix them thoroughly. One of the common faults of the amateur is to neglect this phase of the operation feeling that a really thorough mixing can be accomplished more easily after the water is added. While this might be easier, you'll get a better mixture and a stronger one if the dry materials are thoroughly integrated before the water is added. When mixed, form a hollow in the center of the batch and pour in some of the water. Continue to mix by working with the shovel but be careful not to break the walls around the water so that it will run off. Add the remainder of the water as you continue to mix and stay with it until all the aggregates are fully coated.

Although a shovel does a good job of mixing, you may find that a hoe is easier for you to use. The implement is not so important as the thoroughness with which it is used.

Small Mixers

As we've said before, mixing the materials is the toughest part of any concrete project, so when you have a sizable

Dumping the Concrete

Concrete should be placed in the forms immediately after it has been mixed. A short delay won't hurt, but more than twenty minutes or so is gambling. Any necessary delay is the result of poor planning and should be avoided. Concrete, dumped from a wheelbarrow or directly from a mechanical mixer, should be spread with a hoe or a rake and worked well into all corners and angles and then tamped vertically with a rake to eliminate air pockets and assure a solid mass.

If you must transport the mix in a wheelbarrow, avoid traveling over rough ground. What happens here is that the constant jarring and dumping will cause the aggregates in the mix to separate. Heavier and larger materials will fall to the bottom while water and cement will rise. If you must travel over uneven ground, go to the trouble of laying down large planks over which you can guide the wheelbarrow.

Avoid excessive shoveling to get the concrete spread around; dump it from the wheelbarrow exactly where it's most needed. Overlap successive pourings. If you're filling a high form such as a retaining wall, don't pour in one spot until the form is filled there and then move on. Work around so you will be placing the concrete in layers from 6 to 12 inches thick. Begin at the ends of the form and work toward the middle.

Spread and tamp with a rake, compacting concrete in all areas and paying special attention around reinforcement to eliminate air pockets. High forms can be tapped on the outside with a hammer to settle the material inside avoiding "honeycombing" against the inside surface of the forms. Using a 2x4 in a vertical motion will help settle and compact concrete in deep forms.

When interrupting a pour is absolutely unavoidable, take these precautions: Rough up the top surface of the concrete already poured before it hardens. When you resume the pour, wet the roughened area and plaster it with a cement paste before resuming the pour. Another way to bind the two pours together, and this is especially recommended when the interruption lasts several days, is to form a pocket in the poured concrete before it hardens. You can do this by inserting an oil-coated 2x4 in the fresh concrete and removing it after the concrete has hardened enough to maintain its shape. When the next batch is poured, the slot, or key, formed by the 2x4 will serve to tie the two pours together.

A 2x4 with its ends resting on opposite forms is used to level the surface. One man can do this job easily on 4-foot square patio or terrace grids.

A wooden float takes over after the screeding. On big jobs one man will start to finish while another worker is still filling and screeding.

Expansion Joints

An expansion joint provides for the movement of the concrete slab to avoid buckling in hot weather. Such a joint is good practice when a concrete slab or walk butts against an existing structure such as a wall or the side of a building or another slab or walk. The people from whom you buy the ready-mix concrete or your building materials supply dealer can provide you with preshaped material made especially to serve this purpose. Special steel-cut nails can be used to attach the expansion joint material to the existing structure against which the new concrete will abut.

Screeding

After the concrete has been poured and settled into place by raking and tamping, its top surface must be leveled off to the height of the form boards. This is done with a "strikeboard"—nothing more than

a suitable length of 2x4 or 2x6 or even some 1″ stock. The bottom edge should be straight unless a contour on the surface of the concrete is required. For example, if you're making a walk and wish to provide for fast drainage of rainwater, you can "crown" the center of the walk so that it slopes slightly toward the outer edges. In this case the strikeboard would be shaped to provide for this.

The board is placed so the ends rest on the forms and is moved across the concrete in a sawing motion. If holes appear as you work the board across, place the material that's being moved ahead of the strikeboard to fill the hole and then move the board back again and repeat the procedure. On a large area, a second person can use a shovel to move the excess concrete that will pile up in front of the strikeboard and place it where needed.

Floating

A "float," which is nothing more than a small wood surface with a handle attached, is used on the concrete after screeding. This should not be done if the concrete is still plastic enough for the operation to bring much water and a lot of fine aggregates to the surface. Doing a small area with the float will tell you if this is so and indicates that the pour has not set enough. The float will produce an even, gritty, non-slip surface that is perfectly practical. It should be used first even when the final finish required is a smooth one to be done with a steel trowel. The wood float helps to bring up some of the finer aggregates and settles the larger pieces, preparing the surface of the concrete for smooth finishing with a steel trowel or other textures produced by other means.

11

Curing

Concrete does not dry immediately—in fact it shouldn't be allowed to—it must *set*. The strength of concrete is due to a chemical reaction that takes place between the cement and water and this reaction can take place only if the concrete is wet. The simplest way to maintain this moisture is to fine-spray the pour with a hose a couple of times a day for at least a week, or possibly longer.

The concrete can be covered with canvas, straw, burlap, or even layers of newspaper. With the covering material kept wet, the concrete will retain its moisture. Damp-cured concrete is at least 50 per cent stronger than concrete neglected after the initial pour. When using a covering material be sure the concrete has set sufficiently so that you don't mar its surface. •

Float is not used until concrete has set. If floating brings excessive water to the surface, wait awhile.

ESTIMATING CONCRETE SLAB REQUIREMENTS

SQUARE FOOTAGE (length of slab x width of slab)	SLAB THICKNESS (IN INCHES)				
	4	5	6	8	12
50	0.62	0.77	0.93	1.2	1.9
100	1.2	1.5	1.9	2.5	3.7
200	2.5	3.1	3.7	4.9	7.4
300	3.7	4.7	5.6	7.4	11.1
400	4.9	6.2	7.4	9.8	14.8
500	6.2	7.2	9.3	12.4	18.6

HOW TO ESTIMATE RAW MATERIAL RE-QUIREMENTS (when mixing yourself) PER 100 SQ. FEET OF MORTAR OR CONCRETE

PROJ-ECT THICK-NESS	MOR-TAR OR CON-CRETE (in cu. yds.)	MATERIALS				
		mortar		concrete		
		1—3 mix		1—	1¾—	2¼ mix
		cement	sand	cement	sand	gravel
⅜″	⅛	1 sack	3 cu. ft.	....	....	....
¾″	¼	2 sacks	6 cu. ft.	....	....	....
1″	⅓	2¾ sacks	8 cu. ft.	2⅔ sacks	6 cu. ft.	7 cu. ft.
1½″	½	....	....	4 sacks	8 cu. ft.	10 cu. ft.
3″	·1	....	....	8 sacks	16 cu. ft.	19 cu. ft.

SUGGESTED MIXES FOR SPECIFIC PROJECTS

PROJECT	gallons of water to use for each 1-sack batch when the sand is				PROPOR-TIONS
	dry	damp	wet	very wet	
Projects subject to severe wear & weather	5	4½	4	3½	use 1: 2: 2¼ mix maximum size of aggregates used should not be more than ¾″
floors driveways walks storage tanks septic tanks slabs, patios columns	6	5½	5	4¼	use 1: 2¼: 3 mix maximum size of aggregates used should not be more than 1″
founda-tions footings retaining walls garden walls	7	6¼	5½	4¾	use 1: 3: 4 mix maximum size of aggregates used should not be more than 1½″

NOTES DRY SAND contains no moisture

DAMP SAND will not hold together after being squeezed in the hand

WET SAND will hold together when squeezed but it does not leave the hand wet

VERY WET SAND, after the squeeze test, will leave the hand wet. Maybe it contains moisture from a recent rain

WHEN IN DOUBT, USE LESS WATER—YOU CAN ALWAYS ADD MORE BUT NEVER BEYOND THE SUGGESTED AMOUNTS.

Make use of extra concrete by forming stepping-stones right on the ground, as shown in photo.

Concrete Forms

Construct them rigidly with adequate bracing for strength

WHEN you stop to consider that wet concrete mix weighs about 150 pounds per cubic foot, it's easy to see why a form, put up to retain a mass of it, must be constructed rigidly with adequate bracing to withstand tremendous load. Forms must be especially strong for pouring foundations and concrete walls. Rigidity and bracing prevent bulging of forms under load and avoid uneven lines and curves where you don't want them. Form boards (or "sheathing" as it's often called), vertical posts, studs and diagonal bracing must be strong enough to withstand the pressure.

Forms of any size are usually made from one inch boards bulked up with 2x4 or 4x4 studs with spacing as close as 16 inches on centers. Wall forms opposite each other are held together with wire which passes through the forms and loops around opposite studs. To maintain even thickness of the wall, use spreaders (or spacer blocks) between form walls. The spreaders are lengths of 2x2 or 2x4 stock and are removed as the concrete pour reaches them.

A considerable cash outlay often goes into material used to build concrete forms. Many contractors build forms in such a way that they can be broken down and used again on another job. In the interests of economy foundation forms are made with wood which is suitable for use as subflooring or sheathing after it's removed from the concrete.

Different wall textures can be created by selecting a particular kind of wood for the forms. Often an architect will specify form material just for this reason. A three-dimensional, etched plywood for example, will emboss a wood pattern into the concrete. On a job of this type it's a good idea to "paint" the form wood with engine oil so it can be readily removed after the pour has set.

Tongue-and-groove board with beveled edges will produce a concrete wall with raised, horizontal lines. Lining the inside of a form with suitable paper will produce a super-smooth finish. Although good sound boards are usually used to make concrete forms, it sometimes pays to use a not-so-sound wood with loose knots and surface blemishes if the effects it creates are specifically desired.

Using off-trail materials is the exception rather than the rule. Yet the distinctive and unique are the result of trying different techniques. A foundation wall that will be mostly buried in dirt doesn't deserve a great deal of planning except in terms of economy, speed and strength. On the other hand, a seat wall or retaining wall can be imaginatively conceived to create a visual effect that is out of the ordinary and most gratifying.

Forms For Structural Foundations

The first thing to do before constructing the foundation for a new building is to check the local building codes to learn how

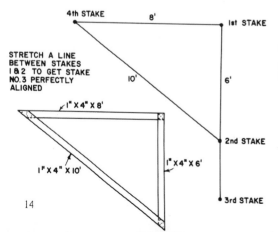

MAKE A RIGHT TRIANGLE

4th STAKE   8'   1st STAKE

STRETCH A LINE BETWEEN STAKES 1 & 2 TO GET STAKE NO. 3 PERFECTLY ALIGNED

10'   6'

1" X 4" X 8'

1" X 4" X 10'   1" X 4" X 6'

2nd STAKE

3rd STAKE

TYPICAL FORM CONSTRUCTION FOR CONCRETE WALL

FOOTING WIDTH = TWICE WALL THICKNESS
FOOTING DEPTH = WALL THICKNESS

1X3 or 4 TOP TIE   2X4 VERTICAL SUPPORT

2X4 BRACE   SPACE ABOUT 16" APART   FORMS—1" STOCK

2X4 STAKE

SPACER BLOCK

WIRE TIE LOOPS AROUND 2X4s 9 OR 10 GA. SOFT IRON WIRE

FOOTING   2X4 OR 4X4 BOTTOM BRACE

STAKE

Forms for concrete pours may seem to be complex. Actually they appear that way only because of the bracing required to support the tremendous weight involved. Note above mud sills have been floated directly in the wet concrete.

The poured concrete foundation determines the durability of the project being built. The quality of the foundation is related to the form you construct. Rushing them or doing a haphazard building job is a very disastrous mistake.

Careful planning of the forms is required to allow for different levels. Extra thought here saves time later and the job of chipping away the set concrete.

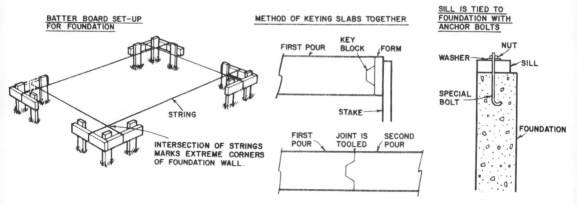

BATTER BOARD SET-UP
FOR FOUNDATION

STRING

INTERSECTION OF STRINGS
MARKS EXTREME CORNERS
OF FOUNDATION WALL.

METHOD OF KEYING SLABS TOGETHER

FIRST POUR   KEY BLOCK   FORM

STAKE

FIRST POUR   JOINT IS TOOLED   SECOND POUR

SILL IS TIED TO
FOUNDATION WITH
ANCHOR BOLTS

NUT
WASHER   SILL
SPECIAL BOLT
FOUNDATION

far from the property lines you must keep the structure. Don't ignore local regulations. A bit of checking might save you from the unpleasant task of having to tear down newly completed work.

The dimensions of a structural foundation must be completely laid out with lines and stakes before forms are constructed. This isn't difficult if the correct procedure is followed. Let's assume you're going to build a garage that is to be separate from the main structure. Set up a base line measuring from the property line or a house wall. Drive two stakes into the ground along the line marking two corners of the new building. Hammer nails into the stakes to mark each corner precisely.

The best and most common way of making sure that corners are perfectly square is to construct a right triangle. The first leg

of the triangle is formed by driving a third stake exactly six feet away from the nail marking the first corner to be established. A second line for the second side of the building is tied to the nail marking the first corner. When the corner is square, a point on the second line exactly eight feet from the nail will be exactly ten feet, cutting across the corner, from the third stake.

Stretching a line from the nail across to a fourth stake will establish a second side of the building. Repeat the procedure for all corners. Another method would be to build a big triangle using 1x4 stock of the same lengths specified for laying out a right angle with lines. Working from one base line the wooden triangle can be used to lay out each of the corners.

Batter boards are set up with string stretched to opposite sides so they cross

Steel reinforcement rods are easily cut with a hack saw, as shown. Cut about halfway through, then break remainder by bending on the cut line.

Tie rods together, use to bond pours that have different levels, as for an overhang post. Vertical rod extends above the concrete for post bottom.

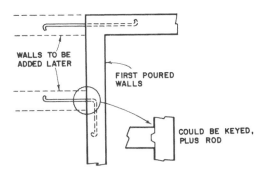

PLACE CONNECTING REINFORCEMENT RODS
WHEN PLANNING TO ADD WALLS LATER
TO BASIC STRUCTURE

WALLS TO BE
ADDED LATER

FIRST POURED
WALLS

COULD BE KEYED,
PLUS ROD

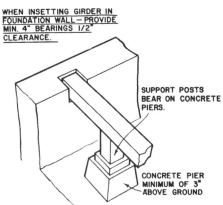

WHEN INSETTING GIRDER IN
FOUNDATION WALL—PROVIDE
MIN. 4" BEARINGS 1/2"
CLEARANCE.

SUPPORT POSTS
BEAR ON CONCRETE
PIERS.

CONCRETE PIER
MINIMUM OF 3"
ABOVE GROUND

exactly at corners established with the right triangle. The lines and intersection points provide a boundary to which excavation and/or setting of forms are worked to. Drive nails at points on the batter boards where the lines are. This way they can always be accurately replaced should it be necessary to remove them or should one be broken.

Concrete footings and foundations that are strong and sound will guarantee the life of the structure you put on them. This means you must carefully consider size and depth before building a form. Footing slabs should always be settled on firm ground and below the frost line. With average soil conditions the footing width should equal twice the thickness of the foundation wall it will support. Its depth is usually equal to the wall thickness. But these are very

general dimensions and dimensions can be affected by many things. Factors to be taken into account include the soil, climate, weight of building and so on. Again, it's good practice to check local building codes. They will give you valuable, specific information for the area in which you live. If you live in an area where winters are not severe, chances are a shallower footing or foundation will be adequate. When the foundation wall is above grade and the soil is firm, its possible to trench the earth to act as part of the form.

Reinforcing Measures

Since reinforcing must be accomplished before the pour, it's logical to consider it as part of the form construction job. The two most common reinforcing materials are wire mesh and steel rods. When used, either

To tie rod to inside face of a permanent concrete grid form or header, drive a galvanized nail in the form, use soft wire to attach rod to the nail.

When a subsequent pour must tie in with a foundation, for example, set extending rods in place so the two pours will be bonded securely together.

17

Low pours, like the one required for these concrete steps, do not require extensive bracing and supports. The center board will keep the riser forms from sagging under the concrete weight.

This house has below-grade living area, so foundation wall is built of masonry units on a poured concrete footing, thus blocks can be used as a finished inside wall. Drain tiles keep interior dry.

must be clean and free of rust scale and other coatings. Steel rods are used in foundation and wall construction; wire mesh in slabs. Rods should be used in such a way that they form a continuous line through the wall. If cracks should appear in the wall, the rods running through will bind it together and keep the crack from opening wider. Wherever rod ends lap each other they should be united with wire. Rods should always be bent around corners. Laps in one-half-inch rods (most common size used) should be at least two feet long. The greater the diameter of the rod, the greater the overlap should be—ranging from a foot for quarter inch rod to three feet for three-fourths-inch rod.

The biggest mistake the beginner can make (and often does) is to rush form construction. He's anxious to get to the meat of the project and feels that making the forms is just a necessary nuisance and an uninteresting preliminary to the actual job. Of course this is not true. Probably the forms are the most important part of the

job and should be regarded as a challenge. When the challenge is properly met the results will almost guarantee the craftsmanship and the durability of the structure itself.

The amount of forming necessary depends on the job involved. A swimming pool with poured concrete walls should be so extensively braced between walls that a mouse would have difficulty walking through. A low curbing with 2x6 or 2x8 side forms could be sufficiently supported with stakes alone. Don't forget on jobs like this you can shape the wall to a taper merely by setting in the side forms at an angle.

Form Flexibility

The beauty of poured concrete is that you're virtually unlimited in design. Graceful curves in low walls can add tremendously to garden decor. If the curves are extreme so that wetting the form boards and bending them is not sufficient, use the kerfing method. A series of kerfs (saw

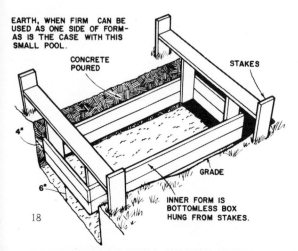

EARTH, WHEN FIRM CAN BE USED AS ONE SIDE OF FORM— AS IS THE CASE WITH THIS SMALL POOL.

CONCRETE POURED

STAKES

4"

GRADE

6"

INNER FORM IS BOTTOMLESS BOX HUNG FROM STAKES.

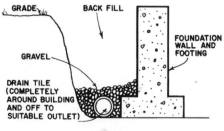

PROVISION FOR CARRYING WATER AWAY FROM FOUNDATION

GRADE

BACK FILL

GRAVEL

FOUNDATION WALL AND FOOTING

DRAIN TILE (COMPLETELY AROUND BUILDING AND OFF TO SUITABLE OUTLET)

18

Gentle curves can be formed with a 1x4. Stock ½x4 inches will bend even more. If these are not strong enough, or if curve is too extreme even for them, use the kerfing method of board bending.

One trick to use on a gridded patio or terrace pour is to drive galvanized nails into the grids, as shown here. This ties the two together and keeps the grids from rising above the concrete surface.

cuts) are cut across the grain of the wood. This process removes enough wood so that the board can be bent back on itself. Depth of the kerfs should be at least three fourths the thickness of the stock. Spacing between them depends on the amount of bend needed. The greater the bend the deeper the kerfs and the closer the spacing. When the amount of bend varies, put kerfs closer together at points of greatest bend. The kerfed side, of course, is the *outside* surface of the form.

Often materials other than wood can be used in forms to create different effects. Masonite is easily bent, even in extreme curves, and its smooth finish will guarantee a smooth surface on the concrete. Since Masonite is a thin material it will have to be well supported if the pour comprises a heavy load. Masonite used as the bottom of a form made to cast stepping stones or flagstones gives a super smooth topping.

On one job a craftsman used corrugated fiberglass panels to cast a concrete project that duplicated the corrugated surface. Likewise, metal lawn edging can be used

as the form material for stepping stones to create some interesting edges. Since metal stripping is fairly flexible it's quite easy to use it for casting round or oval stones.

Once the forms are set the concrete should be poured in continuous layers. Don't fill one area to the top and then go on to adjacent areas. Instead, pour around the form in layers at least six inches deep; work fast enough to minimize the possibility of excessive set time between layers. Tamp the concrete into the forms with a 2x4 and/or a shovel. A flat-bladed tool works best and is easily used against the inside faces of the forms where you want a smooth surface on the concrete.

Forms should be left in place for about a week with the top surface of the pour kept damp. When specifications require that the forms be removed sooner—for a washed or brushed concrete surface, for example—be sure that the entire wall is covered with a material that will keep the concrete from drying too rapidly. Old sacks, newspaper, hay and other materials can be used for this purpose.

BRICKWORK CAN BE GRIDDED LIKE CONCRETE

2 X 4 s

METHOD OF BENDING BOARDS FOR CURVED FORMS

SAW CUTS 3/4 THICKNESS OF STOCK

BEND THIS WAY AFTER WETTING

CONCRETE AGAINST THIS FACE

MORE CUTS WHERE BEND IS GREATER

SAW CUTS

19

Finishing

To get the surface desired,
first make a sample slab

YOU CAN do a lot more with the surface of poured concrete than trowel it smooth or striate it with a broom. Actually, the more interesting surface textures—exposed aggregate is a good example—are more in the realm of the amateur than those finishes which are standards in the field. It takes considerable skill, born of practice, to master the technique of smoothing a surface with a steel trowel. Anyone can direct a stream of water from a garden hose to a concrete surface to wash off the fine aggregates and cement which have been floated to the surface and thus reveal the larger stones. The secret is in timing and sometimes in the mix, but both of these factors can be determined easily by making experimental batches, either before or during the installation of the actual project.

Special mix and heavy washing can result in a very natural, rugged-looking surface, like the one above.

We've already established that concrete is a mixture composed of various size stones which are bonded together by a cement paste. A cross section of any piece of concrete reveals an almost uniform repeat pattern—a large stone surrounded by smaller stones with small spaces between filled with the finest aggregate (sand) and each piece bonded to its neighbor with the cement. The more concrete is worked after it has been poured the finer the top layer will be. This is because the larger pieces of aggregate settle to the bottom. Wood floating, which can be a finish in itself, or the preliminary step to steel floating for a smooth finish, accomplishes that to some extent. It brings a fine mix to the surface

so the steel can produce a smooth finish without any large stones being revealed.

The larger the stones in the mix—the greater the proportion of large aggregate to fine aggregate—the easier it is to expose stones in the surface finish. When you think in terms of exposed stones, you begin to think of what kind of aggregate to use. The common type is pretty enough, but for special purposes even pebbles or chips of marble can be substituted.

All of this is within your scope. However, you don't want an exposed aggregate surface on a patio that will sometimes be used as a dance floor.

In all cases, whether you're following standard procedures or your own ideas, it

A wood float gives an even, gritty surface, easy to clean and walk on, yet with traction for safety.

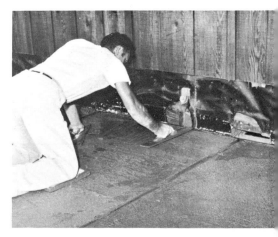

Steel trowel is used after wood float prepares surface. Steel gives as smooth finish as possible.

Slight exposure is achieved with a strong spray after concrete smoothed with float, allowed to set.

Wet down concrete, use little water pressure, prepare it for a broomed finish without striations.

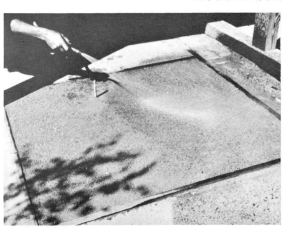

pays to make sample slabs. These can be cast in simple box forms and used some place as stepping stones, so actually you're not wasting any material, time or effort. This is the place for experiment, not when the concrete is poured and you're at the point of no return. Below are some ideas, standard and otherwise, to start you off.

Ideas

Finishing is usually delayed until the poured concrete is stiff but still workable. A wood float will produce an even but gritty surface which is fine for walks and similar work. Should surface water appear, let it stand until it evaporates. If the water is excessive you can help remove it with a broom or absorb it with newspapers. Never spread additional dry materials such as cement or sand over the surface to soak up the moisture. You'll form a thin, weak surface layer that will not stand up under traffic.

Don't overwork the surface. Use the float just enough to produce the gritty, even effect. You'll work more in spots where large stones are near the surface. Sometimes it's best to knock these down with the edge of the float first, then smooth them by using the flat. Once you've achieved the smoothness you want leave it alone! All it has to do after that is cure.

The really smooth finishes are accomplished with the steel trowel *after the wood float has been used.* And if you've done well with the wood float, very little needs be done with the steel. Work it in semi-circular strokes with one edge of the trowel slightly raised above the surface. Exert only as much pressure as you need to produce the smoothness you want. Don't place the trowel flat on the concrete and try to move it around. You'll surely dig in one edge and then you'll have to use the wood float again. If surface water appears, let it evaporate before working further.

Brooms are often used to finish concrete. This produces a finish similar to the wood float but in a striated or zig-zag pattern depending on how you move the broom. The concrete must be stiff but workable. You can make trial passes at intervals during the concrete-setting time, then when the broom produces the finish you want, go to it. Straight lines are done by resting the broom along the edge of the new pour and pulling it toward you; doing as much each time as the width of the broom. If you jiggle the broom as you pull it, the lines it makes won't be straight; this is another effect.

If you've made a gridded patio and want a broomed finish, try straight lines but at right angles to each other in adjacent squares.

A very common exposed aggregate surface is a heavily washed surface. The poured concrete is allowed to set until the surface is still loose enough for it to be washed off with a hose. Timing and strength of the water stream control the effect. A strong stream will, of course, remove more material and leave larger stones exposed. To avoid jaggedness, some masons work the concrete with a scrubbing brush after the wash.

If the concrete is very stiff, and the water pressure not too great, you'll get a fine ex-

Washed surface worked over with scrub brush. Pressure determined by condition of the concrete.

22

posure. One effective finish is done this way without attempting to get uniform exposure. Thus you'll have areas where some medium size aggregate is exposed, with other areas granular because only the very tiniest aggregate have been washed from the surface. This is about as close as you can get to producing a natural-looking finish that is still smooth enough for comfortable walking.

Since concrete is so flexible, almost anything you care to try can result in an attractive finish. Using a small whisk broom after the surface has been steel troweled will result in just enough fine striation to provide good traction. A piece of carpet wrapped around a block of wood can be used after wood floating. This should be washed occasionally during the operation.

Try the normal screeding after the pour, then wait an hour or so and screed again until the surface is even but has the raised lines the screeding will leave. Then let the concrete set some more and, finally, use a steel trowel, but hit only the high spots. This results in a finish that is not unlike the stucco effect often seen on vertical walls.

You could go on and on and probably your own experiments will result in something that will be even better. •

This is a washed surface with an ordinary concrete mix. The pour should be fairly stiff and water pressure pretty strong in order to get this interesting effect.

A wood-float finish will look something like this. Some of grittiness will wear off as slab is walked on.

Here's a wood-floated surface which was wet down with a high, fine spray of water from garden hose.

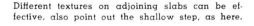

Different textures on adjoining slabs can be effective, also point out the shallow step, as here.

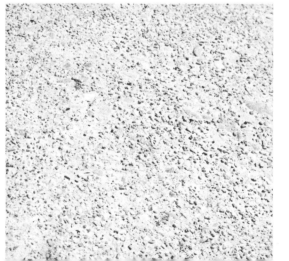

Coloring

Add some excitement to concrete with dyes, paints, pigments and stains

IT'S no longer necessary to have to live with the grayish-white that is the natural state of untreated concrete. This doesn't imply that the natural hue is to be avoided all the time; but if landscaping or general decor of the outdoor room or living area is more receptive to color in the concrete slab or walk, it isn't difficult to obtain. There are many ways to get color into—or on—concrete, among them being colors that are dusted on, dyes, special paints, special pigments and stains.

Dusting on the Color

Basically, this is a question of spreading powdered pigment to the concrete while it is still wet and then working it with a float. This can be accomplished on the concrete itself or to a topping laid down over the concrete.

The powered pigments are a fine powder, available in various colors from masonry supply dealers. They are metallic oxides and can be intermixed to obtain other than the basic colors.

The simplest method of dusting on a color, but one where a high degree of success would be guaranteed only by a top-notch professional, is to spread the pigment around by hand over the wet concrete and then get the color uniform by working with a float. This is easy to do but not easy to do successfully!

Methods the amateur can try with a greater degree of success are by using a mixture of 6 to 10 lbs. of pigment to 100 lbs. of cement. Mix dry cement and pigment thoroughly, then scatter this over the concrete and work it in. How much pigment you use depends on the depth of color required. First pour a few sample flagstones and test your skill and results on these. Using this method figure that 1 lb. of color mix should be worked into each square foot of the concrete surface. Floating the color in will bring moisture

Good example of permanence, durability of modern concrete stains in stained leadoff on concrete highway.

24

Colors can do more than beautify concrete. They can also be used to break up large areas, direct traffic.

to the concrete surface. When this happens work on adjacent areas and return when the moisture has disappeared.

A similar method requires the addition of sand to the color mix. Figure about 1½ parts of clean, dry sand to 1 part cement. Mix these thoroughly then add the pigments, figuring from 8 to 15 lbs. of pigment to each 100 lbs. of cement used. Again, the amount of pigment is determined by the depth of color required.

You can also buy factory prepared color mix in 100 lb. bags. It contains pigment, cement and aggregate already mixed in correct proportions. All you do is spread the mixture over the concrete and muscle the float. Read the instructions carefully because a highly concentrated pigment will color a lot more concrete than the methods previously described.

How About Painting?

Yes, if you use the new rubber-based paints which resist the alkali and moisture that are a natural part of concrete. Concrete will always absorb moisture and this carries the alkali to the surface where it reacts with conventional oil paints in such a way as to soften the paint, crack and peel it, etc., making it very unsatisfactory.

Always ask for the special concrete paints. These come in many colors with complete directions for application. You'll

find that accepted procedure takes more time preparing for the paint application than for the actual coloring.

Briefly, the procedure is this: first etch the surface of the concrete by using a commercial variety of muriatic acid (32 per cent), mixed 1 part acid to 2 parts water. A gallon of this mix is enough to do about 400 square feet of concrete surface. Be sure to read the instructions on the muriatic acid container. They will tell you how to use the acid safely. For example, an acid solution is never mixed in a metal container. If the mix will work on concrete it will surely work on you, so protect your hands with rubber gloves, your feet with rubber shoes, your eyes with glasses, and use the mix carefully.

The acid mix is poured over the concrete and worked with a long handled, stiff-bristle brush. You'll easily see the acid action on the concrete in the form of little bubbles. When these cease to appear, the surface of the concrete will be uniformly granular in texture. If there are stubborn places that do not acquire this new look, go over them with a stronger solution of acid mix—full strength (as it comes from the bottle) if necessary.

After that, hose off the area with fresh water and let it dry. Then paint it—at least two coats with suitable drying time between applications.

25

Stains, paints and waxes for concrete are special materials and should be applied by following the instructions on package.

Stains are easy to apply, are durable and can be used for heavy traffic areas. They'll also stand up under strong sunlight. Color, through staining, is achieved by a chemical mating of concrete and stain and so becomes a part of the surface rather than just a coating. But like stain applied to wood, concrete stains will not cover spots and defects. Since best stain results are obtained on smooth finishes, don't try staining exposed aggregate surfaces or dirty, spotted or painted areas. Not, at least, until you have cleaned and prepared the concrete for the stain application.

Don't stain concrete that hasn't aged for at least six weeks. If all alkali spots are not gone or if the concrete is not really cured and dry, you'll get mottled effects rather than uniform coverage. If paint must be removed do *not* use solutions that contain acids, wax or paraffin. Most paints are best removed with a lye solution— about a can of lye to a gallon of water. Pour this solution over the concrete and let it soak the surface for about an hour. *Follow the same safety precautions suggested when using acids.* Scrub the surface and then let dry, after which the paint should easily come off. If it doesn't or if there are stubborn areas, repeat the lye-solution procedure. The lye solution should be removed with a strong stream from the garden hose. This is important.

Wax can be removed with paint thinners or wax removers. To get off grease, use Oakite or lye solution.

Actual stain application is simple. You brush it on and let foam (some stains contain muriatic acid). Brush until the foam disappears and then let it alone. Work as you would when painting wood—to a wet edge and always overlapping wet edges a few inches to avoid separation areas. Usually, at least two coats are required with a suitable drying time between applications. Most times, a companion material is made for sale with the stain. This constitutes a third application which completes the process and acts as a protective coating.

You can get fancy with stains by making a flagstone effect, for example. Do this by outlining the "flags" with clear shellac, then fill in between the outlined areas with different color stains.

There are waxes, too, for use on concrete, but applications vary so much it's wise to depend entirely on the manufacturer's instructions. The waxes contain pigments for color and it is unnecessary to use the muriatic acid treatment first since the wax will not "take" on a non-porous surface. Most concrete surfaces treated this way should be re-waxed about twice a year. •

Bricklaying

Whether you use new or used bricks, they are permanent and strong

BRICK is permanent, has great strength and a kind of beauty directly related to your choice of brick-type and size, and method of assembly. Brick can be of the same size and type, yet if one is "new" brick and another is "used" brick you get entirely different effects. "Used" brick has become very popular because it has a natural and informal appearance. Used brick can actually be brick which has been salvaged from torn-down buildings or it can be new brick which has been processed to look used. In either case you'll find it more expensive!

Salvaged brick has to be cleaned of old mortar—processed brick goes through a series of steps to chip it, discolor it, etc. You pay for these extra steps. Used brick construction is easier for the amateur to execute because its informal appearance is abetted by irregular joints and alignment. An occasional heavy joint, either horizontal or vertical in used brick is perfectly okay—in fact, that's the way it

Used brick with deeply-raked joints is very natural looking. This kind of bricklaying is easier for the amateur since irregularities in brick spacing and joint thickness only enhance the overall design effect.

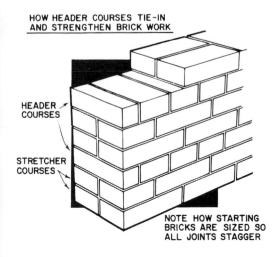

HEADER
COURSES

STRETCHER
COURSES

NOTE HOW STARTING
BRICKS ARE SIZED SO
ALL JOINTS STAGGER

TURNING CORNERS WITH ENGLISH
BOND. BRICK MARKED (X) ARE
FILLERS OR "CLOSURE" BRICK

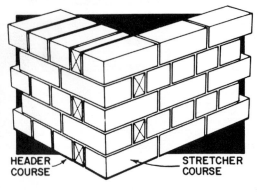

HEADER
COURSE

STRETCHER
COURSE

should be. This wouldn't do with very regular new brick where joints are exact and appearance is very formal.

There are many different types of brick and much variation in size. The basic categories are these:

COMMON BRICK—includes all the ordinary varieties of red brick of basic shape and size, 2¼″ x 3¾″ x 8″.

FACE BRICK—Fired at a higher temperature and with better clay, much variation in color, strength and finish. Except for special designs, face brick conforms to size-standards established for common brick. Face brick can have a glazed surface for sanitary reasons (in commercial buildings) and for decorative effect in residences (fireplace fronts, for example).

FIREBRICK—made to withstand high temperatures, is used to line fireplaces, ovens, etc. Firebrick usually measures 2½″ x 4½″ x 9″.

As always, before deciding on materials for a project, it's a good idea to visit your local supply house and actually see what the different varieties of brick look like and to discover what costs are in your area. Many dealers will have sample walls erected so you can actually judge the appearance of the various types for yourself. The dealer will also be happy to make suggestions as to the type of brick you should use for the project on hand. Usually there will be a choice, so you will not be limited.

Interior brick walls can butt right against drywall construction. Entire weight of the brick construction is carried by the footing that is poured for it.

Brick can be painted, too. A kind of dry-brushing technique is effective. Semi-dry brush is worked over brick surface without attempting to fill surface irregularities, resulting in a very interesting, neat two-tone appearance.

Mortar for brickwork can be mixed in wheelbarrow. Mix dry materials first, add water until mix is plastic, smooth, easily worked.

Mortar

Brick mortar is a mixture of cement, sand and water, with either fire clay or hydrated lime added. A very general formula consists of 1 part portland cement—6 parts sand—1 part lime. The sand should be very clean, well screened to eliminate pebbles and other foreign material. Another formula—one which is recommended for outdoors (garden) masonry—consists of 2 parts portland cement—9 parts sand—1 part fire clay or lime. Use of fire clay or lime seems to be a matter of preference as either makes the mortar mix more plastic, easier to handle and to work with. One recommendation for lime is that it acts as a retarder—keeps the mortar from setting too swiftly and helps to prevent mortar shrinkage which could result in some amount of separation between mortar and brick. You can also use "lime putty," which is a prepared ingredient sold in bulk; it consists of lime, sand and water in a plastic state. When buying the raw material ask specifically for "mortar sand."

Materials should be thoroughly mixed in a dry state, then gradually add water as you continue to mix until you get a very plastic workable mix that is stiff enough to hold together, yet soft enough to spread easily. When you place a brick on a mortar bed you should be able to press the brick into position with excess mortar squeezed out through the joint. There should be enough "suction" in the mortar so you'd have a difficult time pulling the newly placed brick away.

BRICKLAYING TERMS
YOU SHOULD KNOW

ALL STRETCHER BOND—*brick laid end to end with staggered vertical joints*

BED—*mortar on which brick courses rest—also the horizontal surface on which the bricks lie*

BED JOINT—*horizontal joint between brick courses*

BOND—*a brick arrangement that provides maximum strength and an attractive pattern on the exposed face*

BREAKING JOINTS—*to lay brick so vertical joints in adjacent courses are not in line—important for strength*

BRICK VENEER—*a one-brick thick wall that covers a structure of another material*

BULL NOSE BRICK—*bricks with rounded off ends or corners—used where sharp corner is not wanted*

BUTTERING—*placing the mortar on the brick before putting it in place*

CLOSER—*a brick, broken to fit a space smaller than full-brick size*

CLOSURE—*half a header brick, or a brick cut in half lengthwise*

COMMON BOND—*brick pattern of stretcher courses, strengthened with a header course every sixth course*

COPING—*material used to finish top of masonry wall, usually waterproof and weather resistant*

COURSE—*one horizontal row of brick*

FACE—*the long, narrow side of a brick*

FULL HEADER—*brick laid across a wall so its end is exposed*

GROUT—*a thin, rich mortar made to run easily into cracks and joints for filling*

HEADER—*see "full header"*

LAP—*the amount one brick spans the next one*

POINTING—*improving appearance by inserting mortar into the joints in brickwork*

ROWLOCK—*a course of edge-laid headers*

SET—*a wide, heavy chisel used for cutting brick—a "brick set"*

TUCK POINTING—*same as "pointing" but done with fresh mortar on old masonry*

WALL TIES—*metal reinforcement used to "tie" two walls together*

Build up the corners first, then stretch line across opening as a guide for laying the brick between.

Mortar bed is placed on first course, then "furrowed" with point of trowel. Too much mortar is better than too little since excess, if mix is properly placed, is later squeezed out by other bricks.

Ready-mixed mortar can also be purchased in large bags, so if the job you are doing does not warrant the purchase of ingredients in bulk form, you can buy as many sacks as you need for the job. All you have to do is add the water.

The mortar can be mixed in a wheelbarrow and then quantities of it can be placed on a mortar board (which is a small wooden platform) near the bricklaying area. Although you can keep a mixed batch of mortar for one to two hours, it doesn't pay to mix more than you can easily handle. About a shovel-full of cement to 4½ shovelfuls of sand to ½ shovelful of lime or clay is sufficient to start with until you get the feel of bricklaying and start to work faster. This mix should be enough for about 40 to 50 bricks.

If the mortar mix does start to dry out, add a very small amount of water and mix thoroughly.

Laying the Brick

It always pays to lay down a dry ourse of brick before you start with the .ortar;

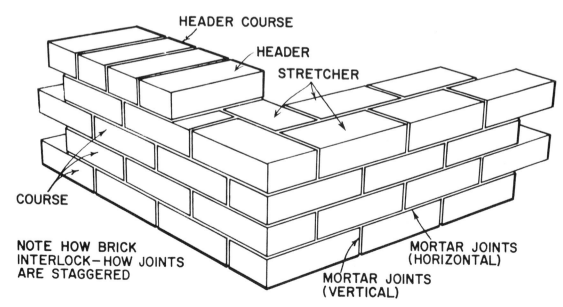

HEADER COURSE

HEADER

STRETCHER

COURSE

NOTE HOW BRICK
INTERLOCK—HOW JOINTS
ARE STAGGERED

MORTAR JOINTS
(HORIZONTAL)

MORTAR JOINTS
(VERTICAL)

this to check if a quantity of full brick plus the joints will cover the area. Many times you'll find that full brick won't do it and that the space to be filled is too small for filling with a cut brick. In these cases you can compensate and do the job with a full brick, merely by increasing the width of the joints just a bit. Width of brick joints is usually ⅜ inch or ½ inch, but it can be as much as ⅝ inch. The ½ inch is a good dimension to try to stick to. One way to get to the point where you can judge fairly accurately what a ½-inch joint is, is to use a small piece of ½-inch plywood as a gauge. After a while you'll be able to judge by eye.

Sometimes, where you can't compensate in the joints, you'll have to use a half-brick to fill out the course. A brick-set, which is nothing more than a broad-blade cold chisel, is used for cutting the brick. Easiest way is to tap the chisel lightly on all four faces of the brick at the point where you want the break to occur. Then

rest the chisel on the line on the broad face of the brick and rap it smartly with a hammer. This is not a difficult operation and you'll master it quickly. If the cut face is uneven, smooth it out by chipping at it with the hammer.

Most often, it's wise to work with a line, a level and a 4- or 5-foot length of straight 2x4. The line is used to establish the height of a brick course from one end of the job to the other; the level lets you check horizontal and vertical planes as you go; the 2x4 is rested on a series of freshly laid bricks and tapped with a hammer to get all bricks level. Masons don't use the 2x4, but we're assuming that you're not a professional and can use an extra aid or two.

Always start bricklaying at the corners of the job, working carefully to get even joints and checking frequently with the level. When you've got each corner built up to about four or five bricks, stretch a line from corner to corner at the top of

One end of new brick is well buttered with mortar, then it is pressed into place against preceding brick.

After brick is placed, a slight tapping with a hammer handle or trowel handle should be sufficient to get the brick into a perfect alignment.

Use a level frequently on horizontal and vertical surfaces. Step back from job every once in awhile to examine it, to see how construction is going.

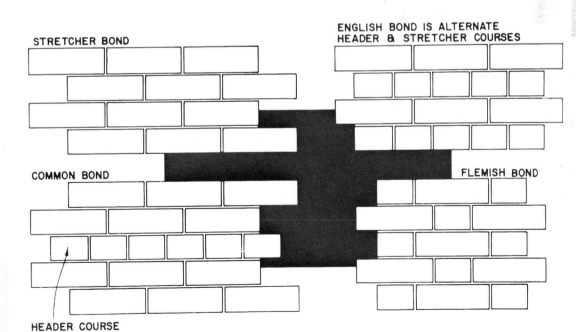

STRETCHER BOND

ENGLISH BOND IS ALTERNATE
HEADER & STRETCHER COURSES

COMMON BOND

FLEMISH BOND

HEADER COURSE

An ordinary claw hammer will split brick. A regular mason's hammer has a special edge for the job.

Tapping down a 2x4 occasionally keeps bricks in alignment. Don't do this if mortar has started to set.

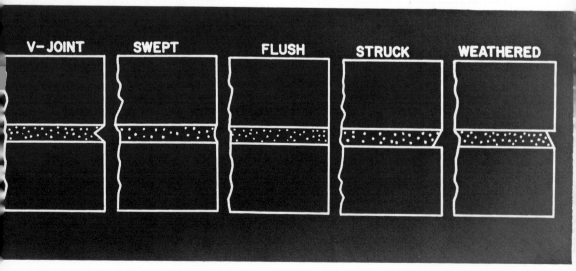

V-JOINT   SWEPT   FLUSH   STRUCK   WEATHERED

the first course. This line is your guide when laying the bricks between. Lines can be stretched from stakes driven into the ground at the corners, or they can be tied to nails that have been placed in the first mortar joints or you can use special tools which hook around the corners of the brick. Be sure to stretch the line taut. If it sags you won't get the alignment you need.

Bricks, especially in the summer, should be wet down before they are laid. Brick material is very porous and will suck the moisture out of the mortar too quickly if it is dry. The wetting-down process (don't soak them!) will also remove dust and dirt from the bricks which could prevent a good bond with the mortar.

Spread enough mortar over the bricks laid to cover three or four bricks. There is an art to this that comes only with practice. A professional picks up the mortar with his trowel and deftly places it on the brick in a sweeping motion that spreads it evenly over the bricks he wants to cover. Then he returns over the mortar bed and, using the point of his trowel, moves it in a kind of zig-zag pattern that furrows the mortar. The first brick is put in place and tapped with the handle of the trowel for accurate placement. This will squeeze out excess mortar, which is trimmed off with the edge of the trowel and placed on the end of the mortar bed or returned to the mortar board.

Don't try to spread too long a mortar bed if you're just a beginner. Cover two bricks, or just one. Concentrate on craftsmanship, initially, not speed. That will

come later. The vertical, or head joints, are accomplished by "buttering" the end of the brick to be placed. This is done by picking up mortar with a trowel and scraping it off on the end of the brick. After a few tries you'll know just how much mortar is required and you'll be able to pick up that amount with the trowel. The buttered end of the brick is pressed tightly against the preceding one so that the joint is full and the excess mortar is squeezed out.

Notice that for both the horizontal and vertical joint *excess* mortar is squeezed out. This indicates, and rightly so, that more mortar is used than is actually required to fill the joints. This assures that the joints *will be filled*. Nothing is more time-consuming or results in poorer work than having to fuss with a small trowel to fill in joints.

If you prefer, you can apply the mortar for the head joint on the end of the brick already laid. The new brick is then placed without buttering. Or you can try a combination of both. Do it the way that is easiest for you, as long as you do a good job of filling the joint *completely*.

The closure brick—the last brick in the course which completes the line between corners—should be well buttered on both ends. In addition, place mortar on the ends of the bricks already in place. This will help seal all joints completely when you place the last brick. This holds for header courses, too, the difference being that you will apply the mortar on the sides of the brick instead of at the ends.

The type of joint you use in brick work

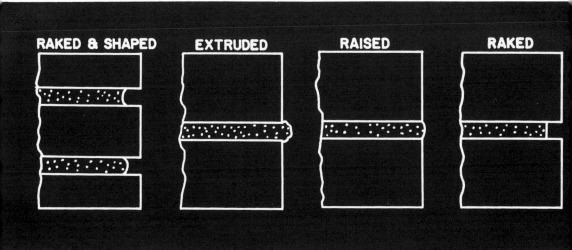

RAKED & SHAPED   EXTRUDED   RAISED   RAKED

A pointed stick can be used to rake joints. Wait until mortar has set awhile, then rake the vertical joints first, as photo here shows.

Most common brick types are (top) standard 2x4x8 brick, Norman, (bottom) SCR, and long, thin Roman.

depends on the type of brick used and in the effect you want. The one thing they all have in common is that they must produce a watertight surface, especially on outside construction.

A RAKED JOINT can be used on most types of construction. Here, the joint is set back from the face of the brick to produce shadow lines that accent the pattern of the masonry. The joint is first set flush by cutting off the squeezed-out mortar with the side of the trowel. After the mortar has set a bit, a tool is used to remove mortar to the desired depth. This tool can be a piece of wood or one made especially for the job (see sketch) to control all

raking to the exact depth. Do the vertical joints first, then the horizontal ones. Scrape off mortar burrs with the trowel after raking.

The FLUSH JOINT is very quick and easy to do. You cut off excess mortar from vertical and horizontal joints with the edge of the trowel, and that's it. This type of joint is better for interiors because it may leave openings that would absorb moisture on an exterior wall. This moisture can be carried through to the inside wall.

The CONCAVE JOINT is easily done with a round rod. It is not very dramatic looking but does produce a weatherproof

When working with used brick, finish joints by sweeping them with a whisk broom. This can be done with or without raking the joint. If mortar has set too much, dip broom in water, shake off the excess, and then use as shown.

TOOLS FOR BRICK JOINTS

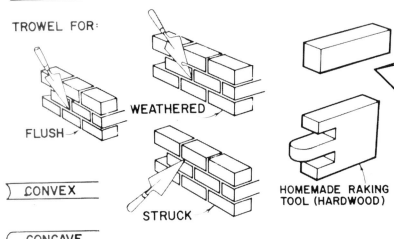

TROWEL FOR:

FLUSH

WEATHERED

STRUCK

CONVEX

CONCAVE

FOR SHAPING AFTER RAKING — USE HARD-WOOD BLOCKS.

SQUARE ROD OR SHAPED WOOD FOR V-JOINT

HOMEMADE RAKING TOOL (HARDWOOD)

WHISK BROOM FOR SWEPT & RAISED JOINTS

joint since the tooling is done with sufficient force to squeeze the mortar tight against the edges of the brick.

Both the WEATHERED JOINT and the STRUCK JOINT are done with the point of the trowel after the mortar has been allowed to set for a short time. The trowel must be held at a sharp angle so only its point comes in contact with the still-soft mortar. Objection to the struck joint: *it leaves a small shelf where water can collect.*

The other joints shown require easily made tools and in all cases should be executed with enough pressure so the mortar is forced against the brick edges to pro-

vide a waterproof bond. The EXTRUDED JOINT, of course, isn't tooled at all. The mortar which is forced out as the brick is placed is allowed to remain as is. The only reason for an extruded joint is appearance.

To clean up brick work—to remove smears of mortar, traces of white (efflorescence), that appear on brick work—mix one part of muriatic acid with ten parts of water in a *glass container* and apply it to the brickwork with an old rag. Do this after a week or two of completing the job. And don't forget that you are working with acid. Wear rubber gloves, protect your eyes and feet. After application hose off the area with fresh water.

Block Laying

Today heavy and lightweight concrete blocks come in many styles, sizes

CONCRETE blocks can be placed into one of two categories: the "heavyweights" which run between 40 and 50 lbs. in the 8-in. x 8-in. x 16-in. units, and the "lightweights" which are between 25 to 35 lbs. While both types are made with cement and water, the aggregates differ and this accounts for, among other things, the weight differential.

The heavy units contain sand, gravel and crushed rock; the lights are made with cinders, pumice, shale or other lightweight materials which makes the units easier to handle and permits interesting, attractive textures that also provide a surface to which paint and other surface treatments can readily bond.

It's as much a mistake to regard all concrete blocks as being "cinder" blocks as to picture them as being always the common

Modern masonry units can be both functional and decorative for either internal or external construction.

Many styles of masonry are available such as the core style shown in photo here. It achieves a light and airy effect.

size of 8x8x16. The truth is that concrete masonry units have progressed to the point where a masonry unit wall can look like the most attractive stone. Numerous textures are available, as well as different sizes and surface treatments. You can even buy concrete block with one surface already tiled. Thus you can put up a structural wall with a ready-made finished side which is suitable for either interior or exterior use. Many commercial buildings use this type of block and they are also becoming popular for home use.

When planning your project, stop to consider the many ornamental types of block available. One type is but four inches thick and looks like a large size brick. Blocks with ornamental recesses are available, so designed that a grouping of four will produce a full, recessed pattern; a diamond or a rosette, for example.

"Split blocks" have a rough, exterior face. "Slump" blocks hardly look like concrete block at all and vary enough in size and texture to produce a very rugged looking wall.

Specially shaped blocks are available for particular situations. Full and half headers, for example, are just the right shape for floor joists to tie into; cap blocks finish off a wall. Blocks with round edges are available for smoothly turning a corner or building up a column. Lintel blocks do the job of a wood header over a door or window.

Any large building supply dealer will have enough of an assortment so you can actually see what is available and make the right choice for the project on hand.

Good choice of shape and size and texture, plus installation pattern, will produce a concrete block project that is luxurious and long lasting.

Some Facts About Mortar

Mortar is the "glue" which bonds the masonry units together into a strong, durable wall. But, in addition, it must bond to itself since each masonry unit is encased in a layer of the mortar. Thus, good workmanship and a good project demand care in mortar preparation.

Use clean materials in recommended proportions. Mix carefully and thoroughly. Never wet the concrete block before or during the installation. Mortar can become stiff before it is used because of evaporation or because of setting (hydration). In the case of evaporation you can restore it to a workable condition by remixing it and adding a sufficient amount of water. But if it has started to set, it should be discarded. Determining which has caused the mortar to stiffen can be difficult even for professionals, so your best bet is to be sure to mix only as much as you can use within two or two and a half hours after the original mixing.

Concrete Block Mortar Mixes
AVERAGE CONDITIONS
1 part masonry cement
2-3 parts mortar sand

OR

1 part portland cement
1-1¼ parts hydrated lime
4-6 parts mortar sand

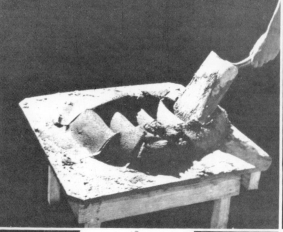

Correctly mixed and proportioned mortar for concrete block is soft, plastic, has adhesive qualities. Keep well tempered on board at all times.

Before work begins, lay block up dry, mark off footing for correct placement. Place the marks so they are visible after the mortar bed is placed.

Each block should be laid to the exact height. Careful placement of the starter will make it easy to place succeeding blocks in correct position.

EXTREME CONDITIONS
(Earthquake areas, severe frost, extra heavy loads, high winds)
1 part masonry cement
1 part portland cement
4-6 parts mortar sand
OR
1 part portland cement
¼ part hydrated lime
2-3 parts mortar sand

Weather conditions will have some bearing on this. If it is very warm (80 or over), don't let it stand more than a maximum of 2½ hours. Below 80 degrees, it could go another half hour or so.

Good masonry-unit mortar should stick to the concrete blocks. You'll often see a pro snap the trowel with a quick vertical movement of his hand after he has picked up a trowel full of mortar from the board. This causes the mortar to stick to the trowel so it won't fall off when he is working on the edge of a block.

Good mortar is kept properly "tempered" on the board. It should be soft and plastic yet have enough body to hold the units and keep them in line. The proper mix will have sufficient water-retaining capacity to prevent the units from sucking out the water too fast after it has been spread out on the units. The amateur should never spread mortar out too far, because it will surely be sucked dry by the time you reach it with the units.

Laying Block

Before any mortar is placed, the first course of block should be set down dry and *accurately* to assure uniform head joints. This is important especially if the footing has been prepared to accommodate a certain number of blocks without cutting. Use chalk to mark the exact location of each block on the footing, then place the blocks accordingly when you are building the wall. In order to achieve a straight line, masons often snap a chalk line along the footing as a guide when placing the block. Since accuracy and wall evenness depend greatly on the first course it pays to plan beforehand by making a "dry run."

With the footing marked and mortar cor-

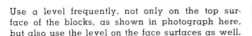

Use a level frequently, not only on the top surface of the blocks, as shown in photograph here, but also use the level on the face surfaces as well.

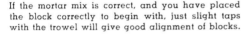

If the mortar mix is correct, and you have placed the block correctly to begin with, just slight taps with the trowel will give good alignment of blocks.

Use enough bed mortar to assure that the weight and placement of the block will squeeze out excess mortar on both sides of the shell faces.

rectly prepared, cover the footing with a full bed of mortar to guarantee a strong bond for the first course. Place the corner block first, making sure of a ⅜-inch joint and correct placement relative to the chalk line and the marks. One end of each of the following blocks is buttered with mortar and then squeezed up against the preceding block to provide the ⅜-inch joint. One trick professionals use is to stand three or four blocks on end. Then the mason butters the vertical face shells of the blocks in one operation. Then each block is brought to its position and pressed down into the mortar bed against the preceding block.

Check each block to be sure all mortar joints are full and uniform. No cracks should be visible between block and mortar. If the block must be shifted or adjusted, be sure to do this while the mortar is soft and plastic enough to make a correct bond. Changing the position of the block after the mortar has stiffened will break the bond and results in cracks. If you've made an error and must change the block position, be sure to scrape off all set mortar

and apply a fresh batch before resetting the block.

All joints should be full when the block is placed. If you do find a skimpy joint, be sure to fill it immediately, while the mortar is still workable. Use a level frequently, at least once after each three or four blocks. Check for horizontal alignment for vertical placement. Use the wooden end of the trowel to tap the blocks into exact position.

Following the first course, mortar is used only on the horizontal face shells of the block. The vertical joints are made by applying mortar to one end of the block being placed. After the first course is laid build up each corner of the wall three to five courses. This makes sense, since careful placement of the corner blocks provides a guide for the continuation of the courses between corners. As you lay each course at the corner, check for horizontal and vertical alignment with a level and don't proceed to the next block until you are absolutely sure of the one you're working on. Only thus can you be assured of true, straight walls. Some masons will mark a

A neat trick to assure a filled vertical joint: back up the joint with a hammer handle or something similar, then force mortar into the joint.

Concrete block can be cut with a chisel and hammer. After cutting, dress up edges carefully by chipping with the sharp end of a mason's hammer.

stick to provide an accurate method of finding the top of each course. This is called a "course pole" and helps to maintain uniform joint thickness.

To guide you when filling in courses between corners, stretch a line from corner to corner for each course. The top, outside edge of each succeeding block is placed even with the line. But don't depend on the line entirely: continue to check with the level as you go along.

If you've never placed a block before it's a good idea to go through a few practice runs; building up a small section of the wall and then tearing it down and scraping off the mortar. How you put the block in place is important and a trial session will give you some practice doing this. It isn't important how you grip and lift the block so long as you place it as nearly correct as possible to avoid excessive shifting and adjustment after it has made contact with the mortar.

Don't try to spread the bed mortar too far ahead of the block you're working on. It will stiffen and lose its adhesiveness and strength. As the blocks are laid cut off the excess mortar, squeezed from the joints, with the side of the trowel and flip it back to the mortar board. It can be worked with the mortar and made use of.

The last block to be placed is called a "closure" block; it completes the course between corners. When placing this block, butter all edges of the opening as well as all four edges of the block itself, then lower the block carefully into place being sure that none of the mortar is knocked out of place.

The mortar joints should be tooled as soon as the mortar has set sufficiently. One way to check is to press your thumb against the joint. If it leaves a print, the mortar is ready. Common joints are concave, or V-shape. The first can be accomplished with a piece of wood, double-beveled along one edge to form a "V." Another way would be to use a piece of $\frac{1}{2}$-inch square steel rod. After tooling, rub carefully across the joints with a piece of burlap or with the edge of the trowel to remove the mortar "burrs."

There are many ways to cap a concrete block wall. A wooden plate can be anchored to the top of the wall by setting $\frac{1}{2}$-inch anchor bolts in the cores of the top two courses and filling them with concrete or mortar. Blocks below that can be stuffed with newspaper to hold the fill, or expanded metal lath can be placed in the joint to do the same job. The threaded end of the bolt should, of course, extend above the top of the wall.

Solid blocks are available for sealing off the top of a hollow masonry wall in a very decorative manner, and these are merely set in a full mortar bed. Strips of metal lath can also be set in the last horizontal joint. Then, after the final course is placed, you merely fill the top cavities with concrete or mortar flush to the top of the wall. •

A special tool is available to provide a V-joint, but a piece of wood can be prepared to accomplish the same thing, as shown in the photograph at left.

A concrete block wall can be prettied up and weather-proofed with special cement paints like Cementico. Buy in variety of colors. Durable bond.

43

Walls

Use them as fences, furniture, barbecues, sound insulators, and soil retainers

IT'S true that masonry walls do the same job as wooden fences, but so much more can be accomplished with masonry that it's foolish to put them in the same category. A low brick wall installed primarily to outline a terrace or patio is like a built-in piece of outdoor furniture because it's wide enough to sit on and can be used as a table to hold plates and glasses. A stone wall can back up a barbecue grill, bounce away unwanted sound from a near-by street, hide the neighbors' clutter, hold back soil at the base of a slope, retain water for a small or large pool or be a planter base for a screen made of another material.

Textures and appearances are as unlimited as the materials available for building walls. Brick is usable in any number of ways as are cement and concrete block. Also available are adobe block, field stone,

cut stone and poured concrete. Combinations of these materials offer even greater possibilities.

Construction of almost any wall is within the scope of the homecraftsman. You can often get help on specifications through the local building inspector due to the fact that masonry walls usually fall within the jurisdiction of local building codes. Rather than regard this as a hindrance, look upon it as free professional help, for if you follow the specs required—as to height, footing, size, etc.—you'll end up with a well-constructed wall.

Selecting Material

The material you select depends upon the appearance desired (formal, rustic, natural), the amount of time you have to do the job and how much money you want

Combination of stone-wall planter with wood frame-work for basketweave treatment of Filon plastic panels, creates handsome windbreak, affords privacy.

This brick wall, which is the front wall of a planter, extends the house line, provides beginning of a screen for patio beyond.

Low-brick walls needn't be more than one-brick thick. Washed surface of concrete patio, brick walls and brick veneering unite the whole area, as shown.

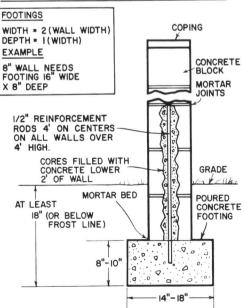

TYPICAL CONCRETE BLOCK WALL CONSTRUCTION

FOOTINGS

WIDTH = 2 (WALL WIDTH)
DEPTH = 1 (WIDTH)
EXAMPLE

8" WALL NEEDS
FOOTING 16" WIDE
X 8" DEEP

COPING

CONCRETE BLOCK

MORTAR JOINTS

1/2" REINFORCEMENT RODS 4' ON CENTERS ON ALL WALLS OVER 4' HIGH.

CORES FILLED WITH CONCRETE LOWER 2' OF WALL

GRADE

MORTAR BED

AT LEAST 18" (OR BELOW FROST LINE)

POURED CONCRETE FOOTING

8"-10"

14"-18"

A long wall like this, though not a week-end job, is surprisingly easy to construct. It is permanent and acts as a sight and sound barrier. Plantings against wall relieve severity of repetitive pattern.

45

MAKE A "BATTER" BOARD

SET-BACK REGULAR WALLS 1/2" PER.FT.
SET-BACK RETAINING WALLS 1" PER.FT.

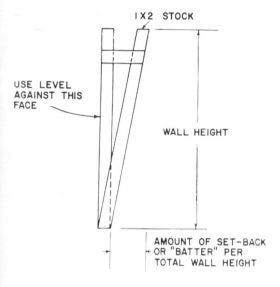

1X2 STOCK

USE LEVEL
AGAINST THIS
FACE

WALL HEIGHT

AMOUNT OF SET-BACK
OR "BATTER" PER
TOTAL WALL HEIGHT

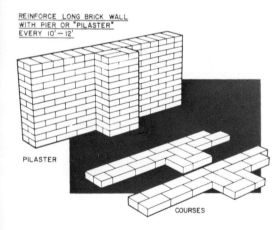

REINFORCE LONG BRICK WALL
WITH PIER OR "PILASTER"
EVERY 10'—12'

PILASTER

COURSES

to spend. Concrete is economical to use, and most of the time and work involved is in construction of forms. You'll have the pleasure of seeing the entire wall poured at one time when the forms are complete. Remember, however, a project of this type is no little sidewalk. A wall of concrete, even one of a low three feet, has tremendous weight, and forms will have to be well-constructed and adequately braced to contain the material until it has set.

Concrete block will produce a sturdy and economical wall and the big 8″x8″x16″ blocks make for fast construction. You don't have to stick to the plain blocks. A catalog from any manufacturer will reveal numerous sizes, shapes and surface textures—some so unlike the usual block surfaces that they present a completely different appearance. The method of laying block will also affect appearance. You don't have to stick to a common running bond. Combining blocks of different sizes leads to imaginative treatment. The techniques of laying block for walls is the same as the methods described in the chapter on concrete block. The top course should be sealed and guarded from moisture. This can be accomplished simply by filling the cores and plastering on a smooth topping of cement. To keep the fill concrete from falling to the bottom, stuff the cores with crumpled newspapers and fill on top of this. The top course can also be covered with precast concrete slabs, brick, a wood top to serve as a bench, etc. The block can be painted or left as is.

Brick is another natural for walls. As with block, you can tackle a good size project by doing it a little at a time. A brick wall will go slower than block because the units are so much smaller. Then too, any wall more than 18 inches high should be a minimum of two bricks (eight inches thick) which means you must build two walls back-to-back, interlocking them with header courses.

Concrete masonry in 8-8-8-inch dimensions are laid in stacked bond pattern. Deeply racked mortar joints create shadow lines. Note how blocks at left end of wall were laid on sides so cores will admit both light and breezes.

Masonry units used here are 4x8x16-inch laid in a lattice pattern for privacy without restricting light, air.

To break harsh house corner and direct traffic, try a small wall. Used brick makes good topping.

A solid masonry wall gives the feeling of greater privacy to an open patio or to a concrete deck.

Ordinary bricklaying techniques are used in laying a brick wall. As with block there are many different styles and sizes of brick from which to choose. The wall, if built of uniform wire-cut bricks and fastidiously laid, can be very formal. Used brick, with less attention paid to joint appearance and uniformity, can look natural and rustic. The surface smoothness of the wall can be broken by making an occasional brick jut forward.

Working With Stone

Although stone walls are a real challenge, the homecraftsman can achieve maximum success through patience and careful planning. A skilled stoneworker can put natural stones together with joints so thin it appears that each stone was specifically cut to fit into place.

If you have a lot of stone nearby and can pick it up for the taking, you're lucky, as any kind of stone can be used in a wall. Uncut stones, used as nature made them, are fitted into the structure as uniformly as possible; each stone keyed in place. This type of structure is usually referred to as being a "rubble" wall. When you buy stones precut with enough uniformity to allow some formality in assembly (like brick or block), the wall is usually referred to as "ashlar." These terms don't identify

Occasional projecting blocks relieve the plainness of this masonry wall. The planters are blocks, too, with sealed bottom surfaces. Very handsome.

Imaginative use of masonry units can create distinctive designs. Many types of blocks are available, so check dealers carefully for patterns.

walls, but kinds of stonework. The same patterns (which is what they are) can be found on housefronts as veneers and in foundation walls made of stone instead of poured concrete. Many fireplace facades and hearths fall into one of these two categories.

The rubble is by far the cheapest of the two. For one thing, you can use field stone if any is available nearby. Even if you have to have it trucked in the cost is quite reasonable. Ashlar masonry is built with stones that have been cut into suitable shapes and for this you pay heavily. The ashlar is easier to build with because the stones are cut for the purpose. Ashlar

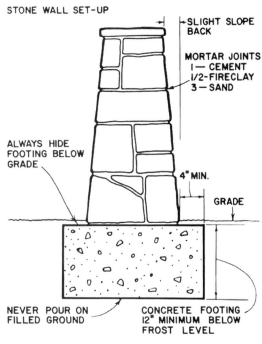

STONE WALL SET-UP

←SLIGHT SLOPE BACK

MORTAR JOINTS
1 — CEMENT
1/2 — FIRECLAY
3 — SAND

ALWAYS HIDE FOOTING BELOW GRADE

4" MIN.

GRADE

NEVER POUR ON FILLED GROUND

CONCRETE FOOTING 12" MINIMUM BELOW FROST LEVEL

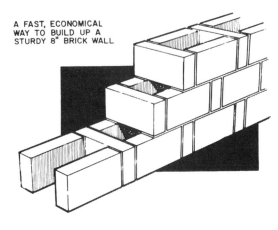

A FAST, ECONOMICAL WAY TO BUILD UP A STURDY 8" BRICK WALL

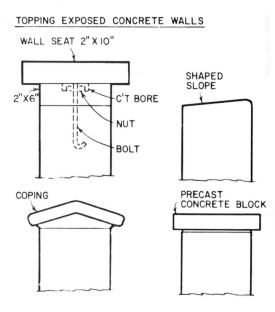

TOPPING EXPOSED CONCRETE WALLS

WALL SEAT 2" X 10"

2"X6"

C'T BORE

NUT

BOLT

SHAPED SLOPE

COPING

PRECAST CONCRETE BLOCK

Photo at left is of manufactured stone, masonry units with very distinctive and exciting textures.

Poured concrete is easily cast in curves like this low driveway lead-in wall. Texture was achieved by plastering after the forms were removed.

Separation between grades is easily maintained with a poured concrete wall. Note the spillway at left for water run-off from sloping driveway.

Depending on the slope, a retaining wall need be no more than a line of large stones laid in a trench. Place stones as closely together as possible. Plan beforehand to minimize moving stones.

After large stones are in place, fill between with smaller stones and a concrete mix with small size aggregates. After the mortar sets awhile, wash down area with a hose to expose the aggregate.

masonry is much like brickwork or blockwork. In fact a good many concrete blocks are so designed that they resemble cut stone in appearance and can be laid up in an ashlar pattern.

There are a few basic facts to remember about stonework. You can't just slap the stones in place any old way and rely on mortar to fill wide gaps; you might end up with a wall looking like mortar with rocks between. A wall of this type would not be very strong since the strength of stonework depends on the stone, not the bonding material. Stones should be placed in as natural a position as possible. You seldom see stones in a field standing up like little pinnacles. If you try to imitate nature in placing the stones you'll be well on your way to a natural, unified wall. The best appearing wall has slightly racked joints; the mortar doesn't appear to have been pushed out by the weight of the stones and then smoothed over adjacent edges. Don't use too many varieties of stone. Colors and textures should be fairly uniform and, if you can keep shapes fairly uniform, so much the better. More of the larger stones should be used in the base courses. This doesn't mean you should use all the large stones at the bottom and all the small stones at the top, but if the greater weight is placed naturally at the bottom the structure will have more solidity and look it.

"Header" stones should be used occasionally to tie the wall together just as you use a header course in brickwork, and frequently, "bonding" should take place. This is similar to staggered joints in brickwork, except that with stonework the staggering is not part of the design but is accomplished naturally and often enough to form a strong wall. Stone walls, especially "dry"

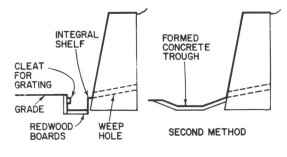
GUTTER KEEPS EXCESS WATER OFF LAWN, TERRACE.

INTEGRAL SHELF

FORMED CONCRETE TROUGH

CLEAT FOR GRATING

GRADE

REDWOOD BOARDS   WEEP HOLE

SECOND METHOD

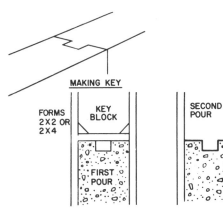
LONG, POURED CONCRETE WALLS SHOULD HAVE EXPANSION JOINTS EVERY 20 FEET OR SO

MAKING KEY

FORMS 2X2 OR 2X4   KEY BLOCK

SECOND POUR

FIRST POUR

Pieces of tubing, pipe, draintile can be used to prevent water from building up behind the wall. Screen buried end of the pipe to prevent clogging.

For smooth, natural-looking joint between stones, brush with whisk broom after mortar has set. Also removes mortar from adjacent stones, cleans them.

walls (those not bonded with mortar), are strongest when sloped backward. The best way to check on this and keep the set-back uniform is to make a simple batter board and use it in conjunction with a regular carpenters level. The recommended formula for mortar used in stonework is three parts sand, one part cement and one-half part fireclay.

For appearance the top surface of the foundation poured for a stone wall should be slightly below grade so the base of the wall will appear to emerge from the ground.

Poured concrete is probably the best bet for a foundation. Setting forms is the biggest part of the job. If the ground is stable and firm you may be able to dispense with them and use earth walls to contain the foundation pour.

Dry wall construction uses stones that are nicely interlaced without mortar to bond them together. A dry wall may be easier to make but greater care is required in setting the stones if the wall is to last, especially if it's a free-standing one. The secret here, as evidenced by walls that have survived for decades, is to have a very wide base and to place stones so that each succeeding one is rigidly and solidly braced by those underneath. The important thing to remember is that the stones are held in place by friction and weight instead of mortar. When soil is used between the stones the joints can be planted for appearance and to retain the soil.

Retaining Walls

Retaining walls can be used to hold a slope, keep a bank from losing its grade, make it possible to cut away the base of a slope to make more room for a patio or terrace, or for other similar reasons. Walls used alone won't hold back the water that flows downhill under the surface of the soil. This unseen force, and it can be tremendous, will topple or undermine the most carefully constructed wall. To avoid it, do one of two things: Make provision for water to accumulate behind the wall and be carried off to a suitable place. Or design the wall with passages for water accumulating behind it to flow through. If appropriate, the latter drainage system is the easiest to build. All that's necessary is construction of weep holes along the base of the wall (openings between the brick, stone or whatever material is used). Pieces of pipe or drain tile laid through the base of the wall will accomplish the same purpose.

If weep holes are used the water will

DRY WALL CONSTRUCTION

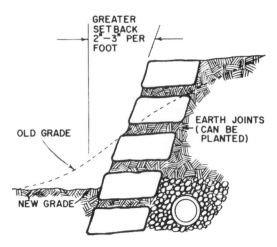

GREATER SET BACK 2"–3" PER FOOT

OLD GRADE

NEW GRADE

EARTH JOINTS (CAN BE PLANTED)

Good topsoil should be shoveled in behind wall. Photo above shows young workman doing the job.

Photograph below shows how a slope was graded into two levels to make a site for a rock garden.

EASY WAY TO BUILD A RETAINING WALL

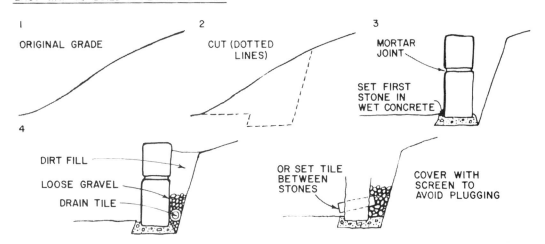

1 ORIGINAL GRADE

2 CUT (DOTTED LINES)

3 MORTAR JOINT

SET FIRST STONE IN WET CONCRETE

4 DIRT FILL

LOOSE GRAVEL

DRAIN TILE

OR SET TILE BETWEEN STONES

COVER WITH SCREEN TO AVOID PLUGGING

Stones unearthed by grading were used to define driveway and retain soil around tree, as shown above.

flow forward from the base of the wall. If this doesn't matter, if the grade is such that the water will flow off without damage to anything else (you don't want to direct the water to a house foundation or across a lawn or planting bed), then you don't have to worry. If you do have to make provisions for drainage, the best bet is to construct a gutter at the forward base of the wall so water flowing through the wall will fall into it, travel parallel to the wall and be directed to a suitable depository.

There are several things to keep in mind in planning a retaining wall. Design can be a complex problem. If you need a wall that's over four feet tall and is to be placed below a steep slope it would be a good idea to consult a professional (who will be an engineer) for design help. Several low walls traveling up a steep bank are better than one high wall at the base. If you expect a lot of pressure against a retaining wall of concrete block, use vertical and horizontal reinforcement rods in the block and fill the cores with a concrete mix. It's a good idea to waterproof the back of the wall. There are several materials that can be used. Asphalt in liquid form will prevent moisture from traveling through the wall itself, a natural tendency since most wall construction materials are inherently porous.

Sometimes a single stone or a series of stones set a few feet apart can create illusion of a wall.

Walls do not have to be tremendous but can be a simple curbing to separate driveway and garden.

HOW TO POUR A TOPPING FOR A BRICK WALL

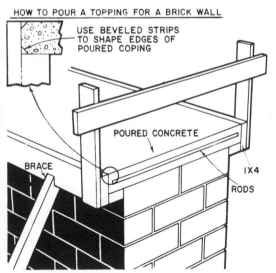

USE BEVELED STRIPS TO SHAPE EDGES OF POURED COPING

POURED CONCRETE

BRACE

1X4

RODS

HINGE PINS FOR GATES ARE LAID IN A MORTAR JOINT

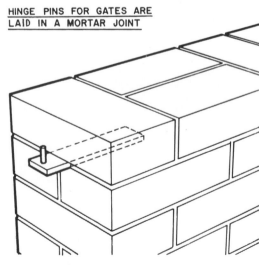

Limit the height of brick walls—five feet is about maximum. A brick retaining wall will have greater strength if the brick courses are set back slightly as you build up. One way to reinforce a brick wall as a whole is to use a rod bent into a small hook at one end and a larger hook at the other. Encase the large hook in a ball or block of poured concrete (or set it in a concrete block and fill the core with concrete). Bury the block end in the hill beyond the wall and set the other end into a mortar joint in the brick. A device of this type can be used to make a wall strong enough to support the weight of the soil behind it. The rod support, known as a "deadman," can be used effectively on almost any type wall.

Of course a retaining wall isn't limited to concrete, brick, block or stone. Wood or wood in combination with other materials can be used. An effective and interesting wall can be formed by casting concrete piers along the wall line, using forms that will leave a vertical groove on each side of the pier. The next step is to let in 2x6's or 2x8's between the piers with ends fitting the cast grooves. Surplus or used railway ties are often used to hold back or contain a slope. Often they're simply staggered along a slope with stakes driven into the ground to hold the ties, which in turn keep the soil from washing down the hillside. •

Concrete block units can be used to protect sloping land. Block should be laid firmly in the ground and filled with good soil or gravel—soil if you wish to plant flowers in the cores, gravel just for the effect.

Exterior grade fir plywood shelters a loose gravel floor to serve double duty as a carport and outdoor entertainment center. Headers on sides (2x4s) confine gravel to area.

Patios and Terraces

They're highly recommended for comfort and attractive appearance

IN THIS day of indoor-outdoor living a well designed and constructed patio is an indispensable asset to any home—not only for your own enjoyment but to increase the value of your home and keep it up to current standards.

A good deal of thinking should go into the placement of your "outdoor living area" before you actually begin construction. If you like a lot of sun this should be taken into account in deciding on the exact location for a patio. Of course this can't always be the one deciding factor. Layout of the house must be considered, size of the lot and so on. Ideal placement is often achieved in such a manner that the patio seems to be an extension of the living area of the house itself. With indoor-outdoor rooms of this type, a few steps can put you outdoors without appearing to take you from the house. In its simplest form, a patio

consisting of a concrete slab outside the living room door can accomplish the job, but such barren, unimaginative treatment won't lead to real enjoyment or do much to beautify your home.

In the final analysis, the patio slab should be an integral part of the overall plot plan. Privacy, prevailing breezes, neighbors, number of people in the family, gardening interests and other factors—all these can affect placement, size, design. And, of course, money. But in this regard one thing is important. Don't do with less because you can't afford more right now. Plan for what you want, aim high and do it a little at a time—making slow progress if necessary—but always working toward, and accomplishing, the plan you originally put on paper. This is the best way to arrive at a well-knit, organized living area that includes the outside as well as the interior

Precast, concrete patio blocks make a durable outdoor floor for informal entertaining, barbecuing, or just plain loafing. Site here has a very good view of beach.

Nice transition from outdoors to indoors is made with translucent Filon plastic-panel-covered poured concrete patio. Flagstone effect created with grooving tool after the slab has been finished by either troweling or floating.

of your home—a setup you'll be proud to
display and happy to live in.

Patios should not necessarily be poured
concrete. Often an unrelieved concrete slab
can look desolate and sterile. Brick, block,
flagstone, tile, even wood blocks can be
used, or different materials can be combined to achieve a desired effect. Severe
straight lines should almost always be
avoided. Graceful lines that wander with
the lay of the land and turn away or en-
circle a precious tree will avoid the dull-
ness that can result from "straight
thinking."

Ideally, the patio should be close to the
house. If this is not possible or desired,
make it easy to get to by connecting house
and patio with a suitable walk. If trees are
on the property, try planning the patio to
take advantage of the shade they provide
during hot sunny afternoons. If, on the
other hand, the hot afternoon sun is what
you *do* want, plan accordingly. Of course
you should try to use a level spot. This will
avoid the necessity of filling or excavating.
Don't feel, however, that the entire patio
must be on one level. A great deal of interest can be provided by stepping down
from one area to another.

Plan to leave open areas for plantings; a
specimen tree might be the central point
around which the patio can be organized.
If the patio extends from a porch, consider
screening it in to provide a means of stay-
ing *almost* outdoors when insects capture
the patio. Consider patio material relative
to use. Do you want it as a game area—
shuffleboard, perhaps? In this case you
want a very slick surface, or a shuffleboard
area made smooth with adjacent areas contrasting. Do you want easy maintenance, a
surface easy to sweep? Stay away from
brick on sand, which, while warm and
charming, is difficult to keep clutterfree.
Do you want a heavy, rough surface? Then
think in terms of large-size aggregates in a
concrete pour that is washed after it has
been allowed to set for the proper length of
time.

The job that will please you most for the
longest period of time is the one which was
started only after all factors were considered and the entire project pre-planned
in detail.

Here are some of the pros and cons con-
cerning certain materials suitable for patio
construction.

Loose Aggregates

Although frequently used, a loose aggregate such as gravel is hardly the material

Slope of patio should always be away from the
house. Main headers (2x4 redwood surfaced one
edge) are laid first, held with 1x2 or 1x3 stakes.

for a permanent, carefree patio. It won't
keep out weeds, it's not the most comfortable walking surface, and isn't at all suitable for dancing or games. It's an
economical and fast way to get an outdoor
"floor" down and could possibly be used as
a temporary measure until enough funds
are available for more durable treatment.
The money put into gravel wouldn't be
wasted as the aggregate could be used later
on as a subbase for a permanent patio, a
walk-on area around a clothesline or as a
utility path.

Don't overlook the possibilities of gravel
as a companion material. A large concrete
surface can be effectively and attractively
broken up with occasional squares filled
with colored gravel. A gravel terrace, if its
appearance and texture invites their use,
can be spotted with precast stepping
stones or flagstones. An open square
around a patio-centered tree can be filled
with loose gravel to keep dirt down and
as a mulch to retain moisture. A path of
concrete or brick lined on each side with
loose aggregate is attractive. The gravel
will also help keep adjacent soil and mud
off the walk or patio.

Since gravel is available in different
sizes you can choose the most suitable.
Very small pieces (pea gravel) is likely to

Measure exactly on the centers between main headers. Drive in stake or sharp tool so that line can be stretched taut for alignment of other grids.

Slope of headers must be the same, top surfaces must be level. Check this by spanning with straight 2x4 and resting carpenter's level on top.

An indoor-outdoor room (photo below) is unified by using same flooring material in room and on terrace.

When step projects into patio area, carry its lines forward with headers even if you have to fudge a few inches. This won't be noticed in final product.

Use a sharp saw to cut the grid woodwork. Professional workmen cut at a very slight angle to be sure that the exposed edges butt together firmly.

be carried into the house or elsewhere because it sticks to shoes. Very large sizes are tough to walk on. If you are going to lay gravel, do it in a way that will provide maximum durability. Put it down in layers, raking smooth, wetting and tamping or rolling. Do this about three times to build up a layer at least two inches thick. It won't last forever, but if you occasionally rake its surface, wet it and roll it you'll be able to maintain a neat and serviceable floor.

Poured Concrete

The number of poured concrete patios indicates that here is a wonderful material for a patio or terrace. They are easy to walk on, flexible for texturing, easy to form, durable, economical and not difficult for the home craftsman. Of course any patio worthy of the name involves a good deal of wet concrete and this is the only drawback. The difficulties in laying concrete are directly proportional to the amount which must be poured at one time. One way to overcome this is to do all the grading and form setting yourself and then call in professional help for the pouring and finishing. You'll easily save 50 per cent of the cost this way and still have the satisfaction of knowing that the design and planning was yours. All you gave up in constructing

your stunning patio was some heavy labor.

A pretty and very practical method of getting concrete down is to plan a gridded effect. This simply means that you set down 2x4 forms in a pattern of four-foot squares. This not only provides a decorative surface, but enables you to regulate the amount of concrete work you care to do at one given time. Using this treatment you could plan to build a good-size patio over a long period of time—actually enlarging it each year by merely tacking on more grids to the original form. Working this way you can mix the concrete yourself in a wheelbarrow, a concrete mixing trough or in a portable mixer available on a rental basis.

The surface of the concrete can be treated in numerous ways ranging from slick (for shuffle board or dancing) to really rough (heavy exposed aggregate). It can be colored either integrally while the mixture is still wet or later on after the concrete has cured and hardened.

A large ungridded patio surface can be given a flagstone effect by working irregular lines through it with a grooving tool. By using flexible permanent dividers you can make bends to get away from the straight and square design of the grids described above.

When patio abuts house, consider planting strips or raised planters between slab and vertical wall. Green foliage, flowers, pretty stones and pieces of driftwood lend interest, enhance appearance of area.

An occasional open square in a large poured concrete patio breaks up areas, lends interest. A tree or shrub can be planted, too, and rocks added.

Bricks can be used in patio building without obtrusiveness because of their small scale. They make a good durable patio, but generally speaking are not as easy to keep clean as smooth concrete, especially if you lay them on sand. Only strict formality and perfect alignment, especially on the surface plane, will produce a brick patio that is easy to sweep.

On the other hand, brick-on-sand is a very simple if time-consuming construction procedure. The amount of brick required can be easily calculated. A patio that measures 20'x20' (or 400 square feet) requires how many bricks? The surface of a common brick measures 4"x8" or 32 square inches. Further, 144 square inches (one square foot) divided by 32 square inches (one brick) equals 4.5. In other words, it requires four and a half bricks to cover one square foot of ground. Multiply 4.5x400 and you get 1800. That's a lot of brick to put down, especially when you stop to consider that a good deal of brick-patio laying is in the preparation of the subbase and the grading.

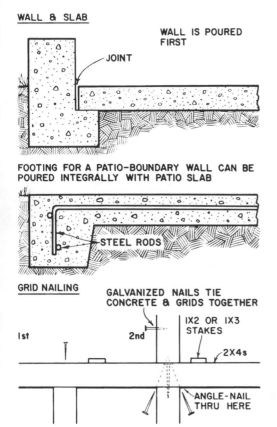

WALL & SLAB

WALL IS POURED FIRST

JOINT

FOOTING FOR A PATIO-BOUNDARY WALL CAN BE POURED INTEGRALLY WITH PATIO SLAB

STEEL RODS

GRID NAILING

GALVANIZED NAILS TIE CONCRETE & GRIDS TOGETHER

1st

2nd

1X2 OR 1X3 STAKES

2X4s

ANGLE-NAIL THRU HERE

Stretched line marks positions of shorter grids. Mark the vertical from top surface by using a square; be sure pieces line up before you nail.

On the good side is the fact that a mistake is easily and quickly corrected with very little extra effort when working with brick on sand. In fact, if the job doesn't please you when it's done, you can do the whole thing over again and it won't cost you an extra dime unless you figure your time on a so-much-per hour basis.

Brick is pleasant, non-glaring and cool, but it tends to hold dirt, grease, salad dressing and mustard. Brick on a concrete base with mortared joints is permanent, but takes more work and considerable care in construction because of the fact that mistakes cannot be easily rectified.

Very few materials give you the natural feeling of brick or offer the flexibility of pattern arrangement. Brick can be gridded like concrete. A brick patio can be outlined with a poured concrete band. The border lines of brick-on-sand can be set on a concrete footing with the bricks themselves embedded in mortar.

Choose the kind of brick for the effect desired. There is fine-face brick and the rougher, common brick. Best bet is to see the different types for yourself at the local supply house. Used brick will make a lovely patio in a rustic setting but it isn't any cheaper than new brick. The job of removing the old mortar brings the cost up even higher than new brick. Generally speaking, face brick and wire-cut brick are best for smooth, more formal atmospheres, while sand-molded brick and used brick are more natural and informal.

Cemented Soil

Cemented soil makes use of existing soil plus cement to make a smooth, durable and easily maintained outdoor floor. The secret isn't in the materials—all you need buy is the cement—but in being sure the soil will take the treatment and in following correct procedures.

First level off the area disturbing as little firm soil as possible. Don't *dig* off high spots, *slice* them off by shaving with a flat-blade shovel. Depressions must be carefully filled with one-inch layers of soil tamped sufficiently to make filled areas as firm as the undisturbed soil.

Photograph shown above reveals that one end of the shorter grids is butt-nailed. Take your time when doing job; mistakes are difficult to correct.

The other end is angle-nailed from the opposite side. Use two nails at each end. Be sure top edges are level. Stakes are cut below surface of grids.

Doubled-up 1x4s are used for curved lines. First 1x4 nailed to ends of grids, second bent over first and nailed. Nail through boards, clinch together.

Careful planning of project will permit inserting bolts in concrete pour for attaching plates or posts.

When you're sure everything is firm, level and smooth, dig up the top two inches of soil while the ground is dry. The loose top dirt should then be pulverized and rid of any foreign material. Pass it through a sieve if you have to. Large clumps must be broken up and the soil so prepared that it will mix with the cement as easily as sand. When the soil is prepared, spread it back evenly over the area and rake it as level as possible. Another way to do this part of the job is to get that top two inches of soil from another area instead of having to dig it up from the already leveled off ground.

Over every 30 square feet of area spread evenly the contents of two bags of portland cement—dry as it comes from the bag. Thoroughly intermix the cement and the pulverized top layer of soil with a rake. Best way to do this is to keep working at it beyond the time that you feel the soil and the cement are really combined—then work it some more. Be careful not to dig down below the top layer of pulverized soil.

Next step is to level and compact the mixture of soil-cement. Smoothness and hardness of the patio floor depend on how well you do this operation. You can start by tamping and finish by rolling. Keep checking for levelness while you work toward maximum compactness. When you feel the area is as level and as hard as you can get it, use a very fine spray from a garden hose to soak it thoroughly, at least to the full depth of the soil-cement. Don't wet it down in a manner that will wash away or pit any of the surface. Use a fine spray and don't stop until you're sure of thorough saturation. The wetting procedure is repeated about three times the first day and then once a day for a week.

Well-prepared soil-cement is durable and smooth and will hold up under winter freezing. You can use it for driveways and parking strips as well as terraces and patios. If you have doubts as to whether your soil will take this treatment, take enough sample soil to fill a form about three feet square and three inches deep. Go through the procedure described to prepare the soil for the sample form. Then test it for durability under use conditions. You should be able to soak the sample and then put it in hot sun and do so repeatedly without the sample softening or breaking down. If the sample doesn't hold up you can try using more cement. If the soil isn't just right, forget it or truck suitable soil in from another locality. ●

Concrete slabs set between permanent wood headers are bounded by alternating sections of colored, loose aggregate. Slabs were precast in forms which were bottomed with wrinkled newspapers. When slab dries, papers are removed, surface has rough, recessed patterns. Slabs can be laid on a sand bed or in mortar on a concrete base. Imagination is the keynote in turning out a handsome patio like this.

Brick Veneering

It adds strength and beauty to a home, is easy to put in place

Quarter-inch brick veneer with a brick wall planter improved appearance of this house tremendously. It added solidarity to house as well as good looks.

Before the brick veneering was done, wall lacked charm and needed brightening. The simple brick-veneering project put it in another class altogether.

AS the name implies, a brick veneer is laid against a standard house framework. Most often it's used in combination with other facing materials such as wood siding or stucco, but it's also placed on houses from grade to roof line. Although the techniques of laying a brick veneer surface are the same as those used for an independent or solid brick wall, the project as a whole is simpler because the veneer is just one brick thick and ties to the house frame which establishes lines to work to.

When brick veneering is specified on new construction the ledge or footing for the brick is cast as part of the house foundation. With remodeling work it's necessary to provide this footing by excavating along the foundation and setting forms for the concrete pour.

First decide how high the veneer is to go. The best way to estimate the optimum height is to lay dry brick against the house. Allow for joints by placing strips of one-half inch plywood between bricks. By following this procedure you'll get a visual idea of how the finished job will look.

Remove the house siding to the proper height. Mark this height at one point on the wall and use a level to carry the line across. Horizontal siding can be pried away from the studs and hammered back to expose the nails which are then removed. Vertical siding can be separated on the marked line with a portable saber saw or

Make a plan layout of the project on paper, then you can put in the footings for both the planter wall and the veneer at the same time, save time.

When height of veneer is established, a saber saw cuts siding at that point. Work carefully at stud locations and allow for drip cap of wood or brick.

A water seal was used over the end of the existing building paper, mud sill and foundation joint, as shown. Veneer footing has not been poured yet.

Brick is built up on footing. Lower courses are mortar-plastered, waterproofed. A 45-lb. mineral-surfaced roofing paper over studs backs veneer.

"L"-shaped clips or large galvanized nails are used to tie brick veneering to building studs. Drive in nails so they will fit in the mortar joint.

cut-off saw that has been adjusted for the proper cut-depth. In either case work carefully to avoid chewing up the studs. You'll cut through the building paper this way, but you can install a new piece to cover the gap. Where sheathing is installed, you'll have to adjust the cut depth to avoid damage to it.

In many sections of the country the house siding is laid directly over the paper-covered studs, sans sheathing, and brick veneer is handled the same way. When the masonry is used over sheathing, it is recommended that a space of one inch be left between the veneer and the sheathing. The flashing should travel from the out-

side face of the wall, over the top of the ledge and one foot up the side of the sheathing over the building paper.

The veneer is tied to the structure with special corrosion-resistant metal clips, which are nailed to the studs and/or sheathing, spaced so the extending arm will be bonded in mortar joints. Good spacing for these clips is about 30 inches horizontally and 15 inches vertically. When sheathing is not used, or where the sheathing material will not hold nails, the clips are nailed directly to studs and horizontal spacing is determined by stud spacing. Large, galvanized nails are often used in place of the special clips.

Next step in construction is to set in hook-shaped nails where a planter wall will meet the veneer. Check bricks with carpenter's level occasionally.

Whisk broom gives good joint if working with used brick, want rustic look. Wire vents are nailed in place to framework; vertical bricks are cut to fit.

To make brick drip cap, set bricks ¾ inch long in sloped mortar bed on top course of brick veneer; wood strip on bricks sits under the house siding.

The brick should be laid in a full bed of mortar with care taken to avoid dropping mortar between the veneer and the sheathing if sheathing is used. Over building paper only take care not to damage the paper.

Outside joints should be smooth to lessen the likelihood of water penetration. In no case should a joint be used which might allow water to stand between brick. To protect the interior wall against the dampness, you could use a heavier building paper than normally called for. Even a 40-lb. mineral coated roofing paper is not out of order for security against dampness. ●

Incorporate false beam in brick veneer by toe-nailing beam end to studs, lay brick around it. Note how brickwork is laid tightly around metal sash.

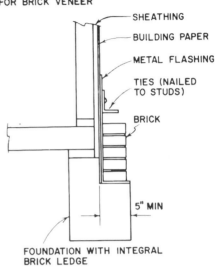

TYPICAL CONSTRUCTION DETAILS FOR BRICK VENEER

SHEATHING
BUILDING PAPER
METAL FLASHING
TIES (NAILED TO STUDS)
BRICK
5" MIN

FOUNDATION WITH INTEGRAL BRICK LEDGE

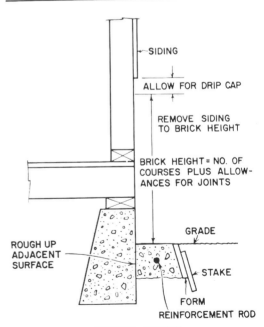

REMODELING WITH BRICK VENEER

SIDING
ALLOW FOR DRIP CAP
REMOVE SIDING TO BRICK HEIGHT
BRICK HEIGHT = NO. OF COURSES PLUS ALLOW- ANCES FOR JOINTS
ROUGH UP ADJACENT SURFACE
GRADE
STAKE
FORM
REINFORCEMENT ROD

FOOTING = MINIMUM 5" WIDE X 8" DEEP

69

Walks and Paths

They keep your property clean and attractive, and they direct traffic

WALKS and paths are the highways of your property. With them you direct traffic. A well-placed path keeps people from walking across lawns and automatically indicates the direction you wish traffic to go when moving from one area of your home to another.

Walks around your home will do much to help keep it cleaner, especially during inclement weather. Good application of walks and paths made of masonry materials will add to the appearance and value of your home whether you live in a city or rural area.

The width of a walk is affected by its function and placement. An entry walk, which may have to serve many people at the same time, should be four to four and a half feet wide so that two people walking abreast won't crowd each other to stay on it. The design of walks intended primarily for your own private use may be affected by the overall plan of the lot. It isn't unreasonable to narrow down the width of a walk if a larger size would be too overpowering in the space available.

Before constructing a walk it's a good idea to draw a plan of your house and lot to scale indicating areas such as patio, service yard, clothesline, etc. Trace the movements of your family around the house. From kitchen to garage—from utility room to clothesline—from kitchen

to garbage can—from patio to living room, etc. Taking the layout of the house on the lot and the movement of traffic into consideration, decide on the best route and plan your walks and paths accordingly. It isn't necessary for all of them to be of solid concrete and five feet wide. Less traveled areas can be made accessible with stepping stones—stepping stones across a lawn with grass growing between them are most attractive. Walks as narrow as 18 inches can often be quite adequate as a paved highway around the house.

Consider other factors while you're planning. A too-slick surface, while it's ideal for an area where you may want to dance of a summer's evening, can be dangerous, especially on a sloping walk. Stepping stones or a walk in front of your home can be a little more distinctive than those you provide for the service area. Here's an opportunity to excite interest in your home and your talents by finishing your walks in a different manner. Such things as concrete around a barbecue (where you want a surface that will be resistant to stain) should also be considered as offering decorating possibilities. There are dozens of ways to finish concrete to provide the touch you want. Another material might also be attractive, adequate for the job and easier and cheaper to put down—loose gravel, redrock, brick, flagstone or stepping stones.

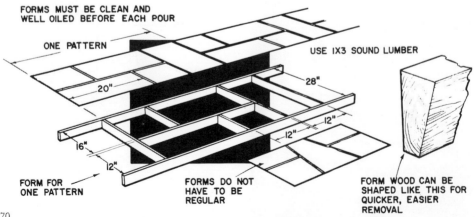

FORMS MUST BE CLEAN AND WELL OILED BEFORE EACH POUR

ONE PATTERN

USE IX3 SOUND LUMBER

20"

28"

12"

12"

16"

12"

FORM FOR ONE PATTERN

FORMS DO NOT HAVE TO BE REGULAR

FORM WOOD CAN BE SHAPED LIKE THIS FOR QUICKER, EASIER REMOVAL

Two-by-three-inch side forms are usually adequate for a walk. Stretched lines between grade stakes establish height and slope of forms, as shown here.

Side forms are nailed to stakes which are driven firmly into ground, as here.

Levelness of side forms can be checked by resting a 2x4 across them and placing a carpenter's level on the 2x4. Stakes are cut below form surface before concrete is poured in place.

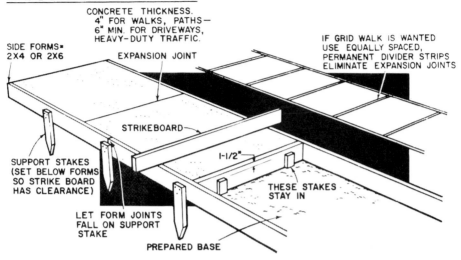

TYPICAL LAYOUT FOR CONCRETE WALK

CONCRETE THICKNESS.
4" FOR WALKS, PATHS—
6" MIN. FOR DRIVEWAYS,
HEAVY-DUTY TRAFFIC.

SIDE FORMS=
2X4 OR 2X6

EXPANSION JOINT

IF GRID WALK IS WANTED
USE EQUALLY SPACED,
PERMANENT DIVIDER STRIPS
ELIMINATE EXPANSION JOINTS

STRIKEBOARD

SUPPORT STAKES
(SET BELOW FORMS
SO STRIKE BOARD
HAS CLEARANCE)

1-1/2"

THESE STAKES
STAY IN

LET FORM JOINTS
FALL ON SUPPORT
STAKE

PREPARED BASE

Grading and Drainage

No matter what material you select for your project, its durability and usefulness will be affected by how you prepare for it. Grading and drainage are most important. You don't want a new sidewalk to act as a chute and carry rainwater to the foundation of the house, for example. The base-foundation, important for good drainage, must be considered relative to the kind of soil you're building on.

If you have to excavate for the project, remove as little solid soil as possible—just enough to do the job. Areas which have been dug too deep should be soaked, filled and well-tamped. Work with a level and long boards or a line and line level to determine high and low points and to establish the slope of the walk. Best way to do this is to stake off the project area and establish on one stake the grade for the top surface of the finished walk. Drive a small nail at this point and tie the end of your line to this. Hang the line level on it at the center and stretch the line taut to the last stake to establish the same grade there. Mark intermediate stakes where indicated by the line. With this method you have a checkpoint at each stake from which you can measure. When you're ready to put the forms in, use these established level-points at one side (or end) only. The opposite ones are lowered (at least one eighth inch per foot) to provide for surface drainage. It's also a good idea to build walks and paths one half to one inch above surrounding grades (lawns, flower beds, etc.) so the surfaces will be well drained.

On a stable soil with "built-in drainage" you can safely dispense with a subbase and pour the material after the soil has been wet down and tamped. If the soil doesn't provide good drainage, if you get extremes in climate (undrained soil and a quick freeze can heave and crack concrete easily), you must do a little more preparing before laying the walk. Water alone, flowing from a large slope and collecting in a confined area, can build up enough pressure to lift a good size concrete slab. If the walk material isn't solid (loose gravel for example), under these conditions you'll end up with a combination walk and wading pool.

The most common method of assuring good drainage where the soil alone won't do it is to use a four to six inch subbase of well-tamped gravel or cinders. Sometimes it's necessary to provide a means for excess water to run off by using a tile drain. The drain line can be placed in the center of the installation or along an edge. The drain is laid in a 10- to 14-inch ditch not much wider than the tiles. Tar paper is wrapped loosely around the joints and the ditch is filled with gravel. The bottom of the ditch should be sloped a minimum of one half inch per 50 feet and directed toward a natural depository such as a storm sewer, street drain, etc. If this isn't practical, you can do the job by providing a sump. A sump is no more than a deep hole (how deep depends on how much water you must dipose of, preferably dug down to loose, drainable soil and filled with rocks and loose gravel. The last drain tile is laid in the sump and the top surface

After excavating, base of cinder fill is dumped between the forms, then shoveled around and raked level.

protected with tar paper to prevent back-fill soil from clogging the openings between the rock and gravel used in filling the sump.

Concrete Walks

After excavating, leveling and drainage considerations have been taken care of, the forms for the concrete can be set in place. Staked-in 2x4's are generally used for side and end forms with the top edge of these serving as the guides for the strikeboard during surface leveling. For this reason support stakes should never extend above the top surface of the forms. One system used by professionals is to leave the stakes long for installation and convenience but to saw them short after the forms are in and nailed. When a joint is required in a form, be sure it's supported by a stake. If the walk is to be gridded, that is, if permanent 2x4's or 1x4's will be used to break up the concrete area, the stakes that support these will be buried in the concrete so be sure the tops are lower than the grids by at least an inch and a half. One of the advantages of gridding is that the concrete is broken up into small, manageable patches; a definite asset if you're going to mix and pour it yourself. Also, since each area can be considered a job in itself, you won't have to worry about completing the project in one operation.

The side forms must be parallel. To guarantee this cut a length of 2x4 equal to the width of the walk and use it as a spacing bar when placing the side forms.

Of course grids, if the design calls for them, are spacing bars in themselves. Strings, stretched tight between stakes, are the best means of setting form boards in straight. For curved walks, use thinner material for forms . . . ½"x4" boards are easily curved. For greater strength, or if the wood form is a permanent installation, you can build up thickness by nailing a second and third ½" strip to the first one—a kind of lamination. Nail through the "sandwich" and clinch the nails on the opposite side. Support stakes may be required at closer intervals with curved forms than with straight forms.

When forms aren't supported by a dirt wall, you can use stretch-boards spanning the side forms to hold them in place until after the concrete has been poured. This is necessary only if the amount of concrete is large enough and deep enough so its weight will tend to spread the side forms.

If you've used permanent divider strips, or if the walk is gridded, it's best to pour alternating slabs. For example, pour the first, third and fifth square, followed by the second, fourth, and sixth. When you pour be sure the forms are solidly filled and the concrete well tamped to eliminate air bubbles. Use a spade as the concrete is poured, driving it repeatedly into the mix to make it dense and solid. Pay special attention to areas near form boards.

As a section is filled, use the strikeboard to level it off, zigzagging back and forth across the top surface of the side forms. If leveling reveals low spots and/or holes,

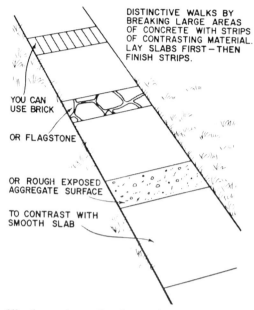

DISTINCTIVE WALKS BY BREAKING LARGE AREAS OF CONCRETE WITH STRIPS OF CONTRASTING MATERIAL. LAY SLABS FIRST — THEN FINISH STRIPS.

YOU CAN USE BRICK

OR FLAGSTONE

OR ROUGH EXPOSED AGGREGATE SURFACE

TO CONTRAST WITH SMOOTH SLAB

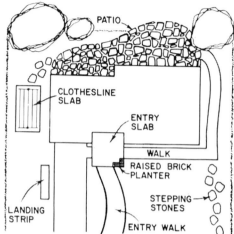

PATIO

CLOTHESLINE SLAB

ENTRY SLAB

WALK

RAISED BRICK PLANTER

STEPPING STONES

LANDING STRIP

ENTRY WALK

fill them immediately and repeat the strikeboard operation, at least in that area. Next, the concrete is allowed to set.

Finishing on walks is usually done with either a wood float or a steel trowel. The wood float is preferable unless a really smooth finish is imperative. The float leaves a surface which is just rough enough to provide good traction even in wet weather. The steel trowel finish, on the other hand, can be slippery when wet.

Edges and joints can be rounded off with a special edging tool. In addition to forming a slight radius, the tool compacts the edges reducing the possibility of cracking or chipping. This operation is not needed if the concrete abuts against a permanent form or grid.

When you have not used grids, and areas of concrete go beyond five feet, provide a *contraction* joint at five foot intervals by using a trowel to cut grooves one third the depth of the slab. The grooves can be touched up with the edging tool. One-half inch *expansion* joints should be provided where the new project abuts against an immovable object such as a foundation, hydrant or existing concrete structure. An easy way to make an expansion joint is to laminate several thicknesses of tar paper and pour the concrete directly against this. The tar paper stays in place permanently; the edges of the gap are finished off with the edging tool.

Brick Walks

Brick walks, especially when they aren't permanently bonded with mortar or concrete, are a handy man's dream—you just can't go wrong. The effects possible are unlimited. When the bricks are laid on sand and the effect isn't right, you just re-lay them. If the pattern you planned doesn't look as you imagined it would you change it with a little rearranging and no extra expense, save a little time and effort.

A brick-on-sand walk is easy and enjoyable because, unlike concrete, you can quit when you feel like it and continue the job when you're ready. But consider these things too: A brick surface is rough, providing good traction, but hardly appropriate for a dance floor or shuffle board. It's not as easy to sweep as concrete and crevices will collect dirt. Bricks are porous which means they will soak up water. You can look at this latter characteristic in one of two ways—a damp walk after rain or lawn sprinkling or a cooler area due to evaporation of moisture from the walk.

The sand method of brick laying is best for informal, naturalistic effects. No matter how carefully you set them and how straight the original lines are, time, use and the weather will destroy this and produce an irregularity that is appropriate to a rustic, country atmosphere. Brick can be formal but this should be accomplished with brick-on-concrete construction so the initial attention to straight, formal lines and even joints will be maintained.

For a brick-on-sand sidewalk first excavate the area to a depth that equals the brick thickness plus the sand layer. Un-

Bottom of excavation and sub-base are tamped firm with a tamper made from heavy wooden blocks. Then use a shovel to spread mix, fill all areas between forms, tamp.

After leveling, concrete is allowed to stand to attain proper set or stiffness. Then it is finished with a wood float which will smooth the surface yet leave enough "tooth" for sure footing on the concrete.

An expansion joint is needed every 4 to 5 feet. An edging tool (foreground) is used to finish the joint. Proper curing completes the concrete walk.

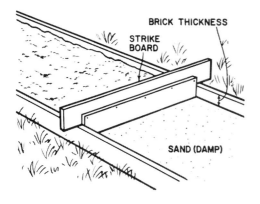

BRICK THICKNESS
STRIKE BOARD
SAND (DAMP)

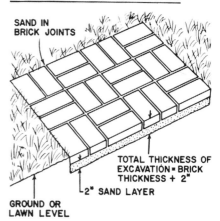

SAND IN BRICK JOINTS
TOTAL THICKNESS OF EXCAVATION = BRICK THICKNESS + 2"
2" SAND LAYER
GROUND OR LAWN LEVEL

less the shoulders of the excavation are firm, it's good practice to use form boards along the length of the walk so edge bricks won't move out of place. When laying forms follow the same procedure for levelness and straightness that you would for a concrete walk. With side forms in, pour the base layer of sand, wet it down and tamp it. To level it and assure a uniform depth, make a strikeboard that can be used between side forms. This should consist of one board that will span the forms and another nailed to it fitting loosely between the forms and just wide enough to provide the correct depth for the brick. The better the job you do on this subbase—leveling, soaking and tamping—the more stable the brick will be. When the sand bed is ready, lay the brick flat in the pattern desired. One trick that will make joints uniform is to use a strip of one-half inch plywood as a spacer. A method of increasing stability is to make the sand bed about a fourth of an inch deeper than it normally would be and tamp each brick down firmly to exact height imbedding it in the base. After the bricks are placed, spread sand over them and sweep it into the joints with a broom. Spray the area with a hose to settle the sand.

The brick doesn't have to be laid with joints between. A solid layout may be preferable in fact, as it will present fewer problems in cleaning and maintenance. Appearance will affect this decision. A dry mortar mix (sand and cement) is often used to fill joints. When the mortar mix is wet down it bonds the bricks together and forms a solid structure to maintain the uniformity of the original pattern.

Be careful in choosing a pattern. An intricate layout, especially when the bricks are placed diagonally, may involve a lot of cutting and fitting in of small pieces. A good way to check the pattern and the work involved is to cut up some thin cardboard into pieces measuring ½"x1". Use the pieces to represent scaled-down brick and plan the walk, terrace or patio on the kitchen table.

The edge bricks of sand-on-brick construction deserve particular attention because the stability of the bricks in the center depends on them. You can use the side board forms already mentioned or you can lay the outlining bricks in a mortar bed to accomplish the same thing without wood.

Brick-on-Concrete

Greater rigidity and more control over the durability of brick placement is achieved by laying the brick walk over a bed of concrete. The procedure here is almost the same you would follow for a concrete walk except that the concrete surface is lower than the surface grade by the brick thickness plus a half inch mortar joint. The concrete is just leveled, not floated or troweled. Brick placement is done in the bed of mortar and the joints between are filled with a wet mortar. Obviously, such an installation is completely stable and offers a more durable walk for heavy traffic. On the other hand it calls for more skill than brick-on-sand because mistakes cannot be easily set right.

A good plot-plan will let you install walks and paths before you undertake the landscaping of grounds. Curves formed by bending the side forms.

Stepping down from the patio to the walk will be much more convenient if the adjacent area of walk is widened, as is shown in the photograph above.

Flagstones

The cost per square foot of flagstone walk is probably more than any other type, but flagstone is a deluxe material, durable as can be, and might well be worth the investment. Be careful with "flags," however. Distinctive and professional projects are the result of careful planning. Irregular flagstones are usually used for walks and patios and if they're placed without regard for overall design and appearance the effect can be rather awful.

After you've decided that you want flagstone, do some thinking about color, size, shapes, etc. There are different kinds of stone for this purpose and your best bet is to go to the dealer and examine those that are available. This may vary in different sections of the country. So, by taking this trip, you find what types of stone are available in your area, colors, shapes and sizes. Some stones are provided in uniform rectangles but they cost more. You may also find different thicknesses—anywhere from one half to six inches. The kind of bed you prepare for the stone will affect the thickness you can use. On soil or sand, a two-inch thickness is a good choice. On concrete with the stone set in a mortar bed one inch stock will do.

On most jobs it's best to make a layout on paper and mark in dimensions. You can take the layout with you to the supply

house and let the dealer help you decide how much stone you need. His experienced eye will pick out pieces that are most suitable for the purpose. This is especially true when the job is small. On large installations, such as a good size patio, the craftsman's hand is the key factor in the most economical use of the material on hand.

When you buy, better order an extra piece that you can use to practice cutting on. Cutting isn't difficult but a little experience will pay off before doing the actual job. Most stones can be cut by scoring on the cut line with a sharp chisel and then tapping on the line with a brick set and hammer. Form contours by chipping the stone away, striking sharp blows with a hammer to remove small pieces. Hit *away* from the cut line. It's easier to make a straight cut by resting the stone on the edge of a 2x4. Cut stones so joints between are not too large. Arrange "fittings" so pieces will mesh like the panes in a leaded window.

A very attractive method of building a flagstone walk is also one of the easiest. The flags, as they are, are laid down in a shallow trench dug in the soil in the most eye-appealing pattern possible with the pieces on hand. Pieces are placed directly on the soil with ample space between, the spaces filled with good soil and planted with grass seed. If seeded turf is available, use this to fill the gaps and you've got grass growing between the stone as soon as the job is completed. This type of installation is not recommended in places where traffic will be heavy but it's ideal for light-duty walks across lawns.

Like brick, flagstones can be laid over sand or concrete and in each case the procedure is the same as it is for brick. Since the flags are larger than individual bricks, you'll have to be more careful to insure that the bottom surface of each piece is completely in contact with the subbase. In this way you'll avoid having individual stones tilt destroying an otherwise level surface. You'll also avoid "bridging," a condition caused by the stone being supported at its ends only which could cause a crack across the middle.

Whether you lay flagstones over con-

crete or sand the most important preliminary procedure is to go through a dry run with them by laying them out before hand for most economical use and best appearance.

Concrete Flagstones

Simple forms will let you cast your own concrete "flagstones" or stepping stones. These can be uniform in shape, round or irregular. The simplest method is to dig shallow shapes right in the ground and to fill these with a 1:2:3 concrete mix. Tamp the mix to fill the hole and then float the surface. This way you can make stepping stones exactly where you're going to use them. For a rougher, rustic surface, let the concrete set for a few hours and wash the surfaces with a strong stream from a garden hose to expose the large aggregates

TYPICAL BRICK LAYOUT FOR WALKS

A brick on mortar sidewalk is rustic, yet smooth enough to be easily swept, as is indicated here.

An extra-wide entry walk, flanked by raised wood planters, will make a delightful entry for this home.

MAKE A STEPPING STONE OR FLAGSTONE WALK EASILY RIGHT ON THE SPOT BY FORMING HOLES ABOUT 3" DEEP, FILLING WITH CONCRETE, TAMPING AND THEN FINISHING TO GROUND LEVEL GOOD FOR WALK THRU ESTABLISHED LAWN.

HEAVY-DUTY BRICK-ON-CONCRETE WALK CONSTRUCTION

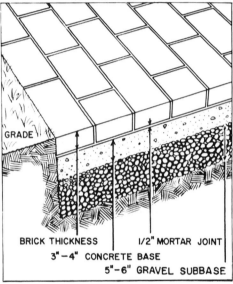

GRADE

BRICK THICKNESS   1/2" MORTAR JOINT

3"–4" CONCRETE BASE

5"–6" GRAVEL SUBBASE

in the mix. You can make the stones distinctive by letting family members place a foot or handprint in the concrete before it hardens.

Forms for casting uniform concrete flags are made of wood, so they can be removed easily after pouring. The wood should be sound, free of knots and smoothly sanded. Before pouring, coat liberally with heavy oil the surfaces that will come in contact with the cement. Each time you use the form, clean it and re-oil it. To get flags about two and five eighths inches thick use 1"x3" stock for the forms. A 1:2¼:2½ mix is recommended with the large aggregate size being no more than three fourths inch. Set the form down on a level surface that has been covered with heavy paper.

The castings then should remain in the forms for several days for proper setting and curing.

A faster method of making concrete flags

Loose gravel is particularly effective at the base of informal, rock-retaining wall, provides good footing.

is to set forms down exactly where the flags will be used. Remove the forms immediately after the surfaces of the castings have been finished, re-oiled and put down in the next position. A stiffer mixture of concrete is in order here and care should be exercised when removing forms. Best method is to lift them straight up with one person standing at each end of the form. Check the edges of the individual castings immediately and repair any damage caused by form removal. Set up a barricade around the project to protect the flags during setting and curing time.

Use your imagination to create distinctive shapes and novel effects. The end of a cardboard box can be used as a form and foreign objects such as leaves, attractive stones and pebbles can be placed in it before the mix is poured. Using firm ground as a form, dig out the shape desired but do not smooth the bottom. The concrete will be molded to the shape of the ground and the finished stone—*used upside down*—will have a natural appearance.

Look around for materials that can be used to cast unusual shapes. Masonite is easily bent for curved lines, corrugated metal lawn edging will produce flags with corrugated edges and so on.

Loose Aggregates

Gravel, dumped on the ground and raked level, will provide a walking strip that will last for quite a while. In many cases it's an attractive and functional method of constructing a path, but it has limitations and objections. Weeds will grow through it, it isn't the easiest walking surface, children will play in it and it's bound to spread.

A good way to use gravel for a walk is to prepare a base of cinders or redrock first. This will give the gravel a firm footing keeping it from being pressed into the ground. A material like redrock keeps weeds out. Side forms contain the gravel. •

81

Posts

They play an important part
in landscaping, are also used
to support fences and porches

POSTS play an important part in almost any landscaping project. Masonry posts can be used to support a wood or cement top bench, a fence, driveway lights, porch lights, entrance piers and so on. Concrete bases can be used to support posts needed for clotheslines, tether ball games, volley ball nets, etc. Masonry materials used in the construction of such items can be made to blend in nicely with material used for more important areas of the landscape.

The easiest way to construct a post base for a clothesline or tether ball pole is to select a suitable container in which the

A handsome cut-stone entrance pier does much to establish visual appeal of house and grounds. Brick or block do the job as well if these materials are more in keeping with general decor. Stone can be just a "veneer" with center of column filled with rubble and concrete. Pipe up center has lead-in wire for light.

pipe socket for the pole can be rigidly embedded. A five-gallon drum (round or square) will do this nicely, as will a wooden box or an empty nail keg. A hole, slightly larger and deeper than the form, is dug in the ground and its bottom surface is leveled. The container is then set level in the hole and seated in place by tamping soil around it.

Next step is to center the socket in the form. Keep the pole in it so a level can be used for vertical alignment. Then fill in the form around the socket with a stiff mixture of concrete. Tamp it and level it off at the top. If you wish, you can use broken brick or pieces of rock in addition to the concrete to fill in the form.

Cover the top with a heavy layer of newspaper and keep it wet for several days. If the form was set slightly below ground level, you can then replace the sod, and the only thing you'll see is the pole itself seemingly emerging from nothing but the ground. This affords some degree of portability, for if you ever wanted to relocate the post, it wouldn't be impossible to dig up the form and place it elsewhere.

For real portability and ease in move-

Don't ever make the mistake of setting concrete piers so low that the fill-in grading comes up high enough to make contact with the wood post.

This is what can happen. If the termites don't get at post then wet-rot will. Solid core remaining in this 6x6 porch post was less than 1 inch thick.

Always set wooden posts on masonry surfaces, as shown. Footing which is required for post support can be cast integrally when the slab is poured.

Another way, when level of the slab is known, is to cast separate footing and embed steel plates to which posts are bolted, as shown in photo above.

83

POST CASTING

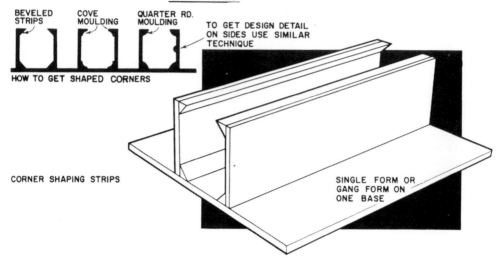

BEVELED STRIPS • COVE MOULDING • QUARTER RD. MOULDING

TO GET DESIGN DETAIL ON SIDES USE SIMILAR TECHNIQUE

HOW TO GET SHAPED CORNERS

CORNER SHAPING STRIPS

SINGLE FORM OR GANG FORM ON ONE BASE

TYPE OF FORM TO USE FOR CASTING PROJECTS LIKE MAILBOX POSTS

PLYWOOD PLATFORM

USE 2-HEADED NAILS HERE

BEVELED BLOCKS FOR POINTED TOP

$3\text{-}1/2''$

GREASED DOWELS FOR BOLT HOLES

BRACE BLOCKS

POST BURIED TO HERE (2-1/2')

ONLY BRACE BLOCKS ARE NAILED TO PLATFORM, NOT FORMS

REINFORCING RODS

ALL FORM STOCK 1X4

TOTAL HEIGHT OF POST = 7'. HEIGHT OF BOX ABOVE GROUND SHOULD BE 3-1/2'

TAPER POST FROM 5" AT BOTTOM TO 3" AT TOP

Masonry units have convenient cores for wiring. Solid cap stone can be drilled with star drill, or with a carbide-tipped drill in an electric drill.

ment—and an idea that is especially appropriate for tether balls, volley or badminton nets—use salvaged automobile tires as the concrete forms. These are not buried. Instead rest them on firm, level ground (or a piece of plywood), set the pole of the socket in place and fill the inside area of the tire solidly with concrete. It may be necessary to brace the pole so it will retain its vertical alignment during the concrete-cure time. Such a pole is easily "rolled" where needed, or moved aside for storage when it is not in use.

Since concrete is almost a fluid and a fluid flows to fill all areas of a container,

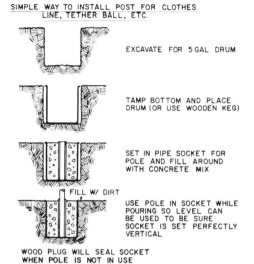

EXCAVATE FOR 5 GAL. DRUM

TAMP BOTTOM AND PLACE
DRUM (OR USE WOODEN KEG)

SET IN PIPE SOCKET FOR
POLE AND FILL AROUND
WITH CONCRETE MIX

FILL W/ DIRT

USE POLE IN SOCKET WHILE
POURING SO LEVEL CAN
BE USED TO BE SURE
SOCKET IS SET PERFECTLY
VERTICAL

WOOD PLUG WILL SEAL SOCKET
WHEN POLE IS NOT IN USE

OLD AUTOMOBILE TIRE IS GOOD, PORTABLE POLE FOUNDATION

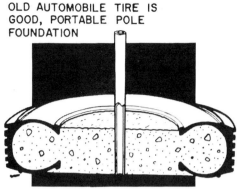

1. **SET TIRE ON SMOOTH LEVEL GROUND**
2. **CENTER POST AND SET VERTICALLY**
3. **THEN FILL AROUND WITH CONCRETE MIX**

the kind of shapes you can create with it are unlimited. A mail box post with an integrally cast, extending-arm for the box is not a difficult project and will easily last as long as the house itself. The sketch shows how a simple form is made for casting the project and how steel rods are used to strengthen it. Don't nail any parts of the form to the plywood platform. At top and bottom and at the end of the arm, use two-headed nails to attach the closures. These are easy to remove when the casting is cured and the form is ready for removal. In other areas use scrap-wood braces to hold parts in alignment. Be sure the dowels through the arm, which will form the holes for bolts used to attach the mail box, are well greased so they can be removed easily after the concrete has set a while.

Individual posts for gate lights and similar uses can be cast in a similar manner. Extending arms are easily integrally cast (like the mail box post) but always be sure to use steel rods to tie these extensions into the main posts. If you made a double "form," similar to that of the mail box post (two vertical posts with a tie across) you'd have a nice project for hanging a sign or a name plate.

Corners of posts don't have to be sharp corners. In fact it's best if they are not. A round corner or one shaped by using bevel strips, quarter round moldings or coved moldings—to name a few items—is better looking, isn't likely to snag clothing of passersby, and is less likely to chip.

Concrete posts are extremely durable as proven by experimental organizations.

Even a wood-rail fence can be erected on concrete posts. When you make the forms for the fence posts, use greased dowels at correct spacing to provide holes through which the wood rails can be bolted.

When casting posts (when any concrete casting must be removed from a mold) be sure the form is set up on an oil-treated flat surface or one which has been covered with several layers of heavy paper. All parts of the form should be thoroughly coated with oil before and after each use.

Suggested concrete mix for projects of this nature is:

    1 cu. foot cement
    1¾ cu. foot sand
    2 cu. ft. gravel (max. size ¾")

The concrete is poured into the molds, tamped and leveled off and should be left in the mold to harden for about 48 hours. When it is removed, keep it out of the sun and sprinkle it occasionally for at least a week. The longer curing time the project gets before it's set out to do the job, the better it will be. It's recommended, for example, that cast concrete fence posts be a month old before they are set out.

Of course materials like concrete blocks, brick and stone aren't as applicable as poured concrete when the post desired is slim. But they do a good job for heavier projects, like driveway entrance piers, columns for hanging gates on and so on.

The construction of these projects doesn't affect the methods used for working these materials. Think of them as being walls. They require a solid, strong footing and should be capped to shed rainwater.

Stepping Stones

Make them of concrete, make them square, rectangular, round, free-form

WHERE you don't want a solid concrete walk, yet require a clean walkway, consider the use of cast concrete stepping stones. These can be planned to simulate flagstones, where a series of different size is laid in a pattern, or as a set of similar stones. They can be square, rectangular, round or free-form. Take your pick. The only important factor as far as shape is concerned is the form required to shape it.

Here you can really go off-trail. It can be very simple: merely excavate the shape of the stones directly in the soil, exactly where you want them to be, and pour them right on the spot. Or you can make wooden breakdown frames that can be used over and over again to make any number of stones.

Lumber used for the sides of the forms is 1x3. This will produce a stone about $2\frac{5}{8}$ inches thick. Any stepping stone you cast should be a minimum of $2\frac{1}{2}$ inches thick and can be as much as 4 inches thick.

Proportions for a concrete mix that will provide sturdy stones are: $1:2\frac{1}{4}:2\frac{1}{2}$. Maximum size of the gravel should be $\frac{3}{4}$ inch.

Flags may be cast on any smooth surface,

Use stepping stones where you don't want a solid walk, yet need to provide clean footing for any occasional traffic. The stones are merely set in the soil to the level of the surrounding surfaces.

Slabs like this can be precast or cast in place. To cast in place, use wooden forms to outline the slabs. These should be set in place temporarily, then removed as soon as the concrete has set.

Stepping stones in irregular shapes and patterns can be used as an almost-solid walk. Slabs can be purchased ready-made. To cast your own, set removable forms in soil, pour, place decorative surface stones.

These stones were cast in cardboard boxes. Pattern of box is picked up by the concrete, smooth side is attained by troweling the opposite surface.

Forms are cut evenly on table saw. Achieve different effects on stone surfaces by laying layer of pebbles, for example, in bottom before pouring.

thus the forms you make do not have to be mounted on a base. A concrete driveway or even a smooth, firm dirt area will do. The pouring area, however, should be fairly level to avoid any slope on the surface of the poured units. If you wish to protect what you are pouring on, lay down thickness of paper before pouring. This will not only keep the surface clean but will also make it easy to remove the stones.

Here is a very fast technique of pouring "flags": Make the form (which is the overall pattern of a set of "flags") of 2-inch stock. Excavate the area to the necessary depth and set the form down in the first position. Use a very stiff mixture of concrete and fill the forms. Tamp it down and screed, then trowel or float the surface immediately.

Remove the forms by lifting them straight up so as to disturb the freshly poured concrete as little as possible. You can understand why a very stiff mix of concrete is suggested: the stones must stand alone soon after they are poured.

As soon as the form is removed, clean it and apply fresh oil, set it in the next position and pour again. Follow the same procedure until the job is complete. Some damage is unavoidable when the forms are removed, but you can make new edges where necessary by using a stiff mortar mix for patching.

One quick way to get forms for stepping stones is to collect a quantity of cardboard cartons of similar or varying sizes. The bottom and the tops of the boxes are sliced off to a depth of 3 inches and used as forms. After the poured concrete has set overnight, the cardboard forms are pulled off and discarded.

Whenever you have a ready-mix truck deliver concrete for a pour, be sure to have some forms for stepping stones on hand. Then the surplus, and there usually is some, does not have to be wasted.

Stepping stones, whether they are made in the shape of flagstones or otherwise, can be colored by mixing mineral pigments in with the concrete as described elsewhere in this book. •

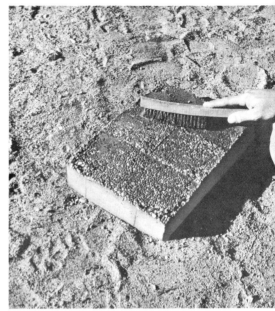

The next step in casting stepping stones is to set the mix in carefully when pouring, so as not to push the pebbles out to the sides. Do neat job.

As soon as the mix sets, remove the form and use a wire brush lightly over the pebbles to remove the cement that may have covered them over a bit.

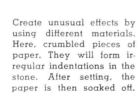

Create unusual effects by using different materials. Here, crumbled pieces of paper. They will form irregular indentations in the stone. After setting, the paper is then soaked off.

Patio table with "inlaid" tiles and stone. Tiles make smooth areas even if the rest of surface is rough.

Crafting

Concrete also can be used to build benches, tables, planters, etc.

CONCRETE a craft material? Why not! The truth is that once you've tried doing things with it other than pouring slabs, walls and walks, you may well discover a rewarding and very interesting hobby. The things you make—ranging from very practical tables and benches to sculptured "what-nots"—can pretty up your outdoor living areas and can, also, if you care to commercialize a little, be sold.

There is a good market for these items because concrete projects fit so well in natural surroundings. Concrete is not difficult to work and can be cast into any kind of shape you care to create. You can even make lightweight concrete by substituting vermiculite, Haydite, pumice.

perlite, etc., in place of usual aggregates.

This is not recommended when you are casting structural members such as bench legs, or where the part is subjected to load as a bench top. In these cases work with regular concrete mix. But where you're making something that will hang on a wall or anything that will not have to support weight, the lighter aggregates are fine. When buying these special materials be sure to specify the type that can be used in a concrete mix. Remember, the only reason for using these materials is to reduce weight, or to attain a different texture. All of the projects shown here, however, were cast with regular concrete or mortar mixes.

Patio Table

Make the top for the table as if you were building a form for stepping stones. In this case the form will be a permanent part of the project so pay more attention to getting good, tight joints. All joints are assembled with galvanized nails and waterproof glue, held under clamps until the glue is dry. One trick, to avoid separation at any of the joints, is to reinforce them with metal angles and screws. These can be installed on the inside of the frame where they will be concealed by the cast mortar.

Redwood is a good material for the frame since it stands up well outdoors and weathers nicely to blend with the "stone." If you don't do anything to the redwood it will eventually attain a grayish, driftwood look.

Make the top of the table as a unit, then, while the casting is setting and curing, make the legs as separate assemblies which can be attached with glue and screws.

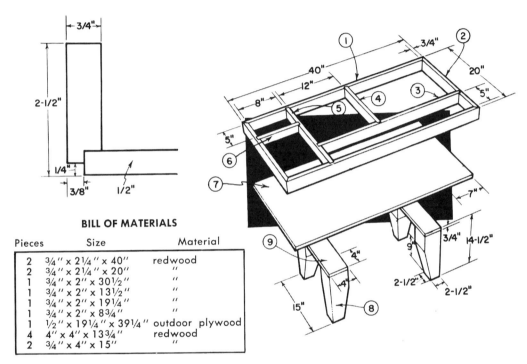

BILL OF MATERIALS

Pieces	Size	Material
2	¾″ x 2¼″ x 40″	redwood
2	¾″ x 2¼″ x 20″	″
1	¾″ x 2″ x 30½″	″
1	¾″ x 2″ x 13½″	″
1	¾″ x 2″ x 19¼″	″
1	¾″ x 2″ x 8¾″	″
1	½″ x 19¼″ x 39¼″	outdoor plywood
4	4″ x 4″ x 13¾″	redwood
2	¾″ x 4″ x 15″	″

Galvanized nails, waterproof glue assemble form for table top. Set form level when pouring the fill.

Hammer nails on inside faces of forms and divider strips; stops strips pulling away from concrete.

Plan the top design before you pour the top. Small pieces of tile, specimen stones, pebbles, etc., can all be used effectively.

Using a loose mixture will help fill the forms solidly. Let mixture set after screeding, then use it as is or get the overall finish you want with wood float or trowel.

Insert decorative pieces while mixture is still loose enough to take them. Place the pieces exactly where you want them to be.

Concrete planters fit well outdoors, are easy to make. Directions for making the one shown above are given in the drawings and photos that follow.

You need a box within a box as a form. For a one-time use, use butt joint, and nail parts together. Don't need to remove inner form if don't want to.

Planters

Concrete makes a successful plant container because it holds moisture and keeps the soil from drying. It is especially good for shade plants which require a moist atmosphere.

How you make the forms for planters will depend on whether you wish to make duplicates. For a single project, just nailing will do to hold the forms together. Where the project requires a form with double walls, slope the inside ones so the interior cavity will be tapered. The forms will then be easier to remove. In all cases, the wood should be clean and well coated with ordinary crankcase oil. If the forms are to be used again, clean them immediately after removal and re-oil them even if you're not going to use them again right away.

Our drawing shows a planter form box which can be used again and again. For smooth finishes on the concrete, use wood which is sanded smooth or use a hardboard surfaced plywood. You can get different effects by using different wood finishes such as etched plywood, for example. By using plenty of oil on the wood and a fairly loose mixture of concrete, well tamped, you'll transfer the wood pattern to the casting.

The shallow planter with integral legs, requires an outside form only. This is then settled on a thick bed of damp sand which has been tamped down to form a solid surface. Set the form on the sand and pile sand up around it for support. Use a piece of two-inch dowel to form the leg holes in the sand. If the sand is damp, you'll have no trouble doing this. Mark the dowel so

HINGED BOX FOR MAKING DUPLICATE PROJECTS

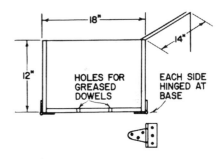

18"

14"

12"

HOLES FOR GREASED DOWELS

EACH SIDE HINGED AT BASE

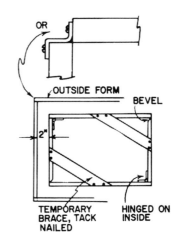

OR

OUTSIDE FORM

BEVEL

2"

TEMPORARY BRACE, TACK NAILED

HINGED ON INSIDE

Put a two-inch layer of concrete in the base of the outer box, then put the inner box in position and fill between them, as shown in photo above.

Tamp the concrete down in layers, as shown in photograph above, but don't overdo it or all the large stones will end up at the bottom of the form.

When you've filled about halfway up, lay in a pre-shaped concrete reinforcement rod. Place it carefully so it will be completely covered by the mix.

Let the concrete set for about two days, then remove the inner forms first. This is the hinged form box which can be used over and over again.

Holding the sides together with these bent up angles permits a very slight outside slope without actually having to taper the sides of the forms.

The outside forms fold down and away, as shown. Lift the project carefully. It won't take rough treatment for at least a week or about ten days.

94

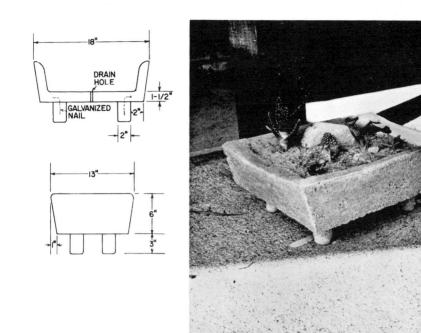

Shallow planter is nice for miniature cactus garden. Short legs are cast integrally with body of planter. See the diagrams for the instructions.

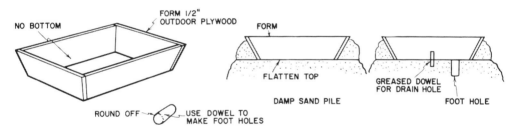

you'll make each hole the same depth. Turn the dowel a few times before extracting it. We used a mortar mix here into which we added some small beach pebbles. Use a little extra water so the mix will pour easily in the leg holes. Let this set just a bit then press in the bent up galvanized nails as shown in the drawing. These will tie the legs to the body of the planter and give them strength.

Since no inside form is provided for the planter, shape the sidewalls up by hand. Try to maintain a uniform thickness throughout—although some slight irregularities won't matter as the inside surfaces will be concealed by the soil.

Many other shapes are possible by using a partial wood form in combination with sand. (See drawings).

OTHER PLANTER IDEAS

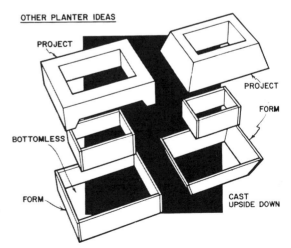

Thin aluminum formed the circle into which this small, attractive, concrete-top drum table was cast.

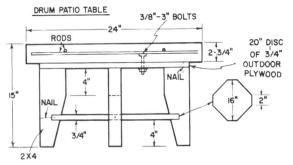

DRUM PATIO TABLE

3/8"-3" BOLTS

24"

RODS

2-3/4"

20" DISC
OF 3/4"
OUTDOOR
PLYWOOD

NAIL

4"

15"

16"   2"

NAIL

3/4"   4"

2 X 4

Two nails driven through stick is compass to form circle. Distance between nails is radius of circle.

Drum Table

A few of these small, round-top tables will do much to dress up a patio and will be handy for keeping ash trays, glasses, etc., close to lounges and chairs. The table's circular shape is achieved by cutting a disc of plywood and then bordering it with thin-aluminum sheeting.

You can get some interesting effects by spreading bright-colored pebbles, small pieces of tile, or specimen stones, in the form before pouring the mix. Use a regular mortar mix with fire clay and an extra helping of portland cement to get a really smooth finish. Make it loose enough so you won't have to do too much tamping to fill the form. When the form is full, tap the outside with a hammer to settle the mix against the form. When the pour has set enough insert the bolts. For extra strength, bend up a 3/8-inch rod into a circular shape and set this in the pour when the form is about half full.

The legs are made as a separate assembly which attaches to the table top with the bolts that were imbedded in the cement.

96

Sculpture

You can provide many interesting areas in the garden by making forms for casting unusual shapes in concrete. You can be very realistic with what you do, or you can make abstractions and cast these artificial stone pieces just for effect and in a pleasant shape that doesn't try to look like anything. Use a regular concrete mix —½-inch or ¾-inch plywood for the forms. Where curves are involved you can use do-it-yourself aluminum for the forms.

In most cases you should reinforce the projects by imbedding concrete steel rods in the pour. Fill half the mold, then place the rods, then fill the remainder of the mold.

The projects will stand alone if they are buried enough in the soil. If you wish the entire unit to be exposed you'll have to pour a small footing first and imbed a few inches of the sculpture base into that. Pour the footing low enough so soil can cover it neatly.

Hanger bolt is inserted through hole in form to make hand-print plaque. Chicken wire is placed after the form has been half-filled with mortar mix.

Hand-print plaque can become a treasured family memento. Use a sharp stick to mark the year when the mix is just a little short of being hard.

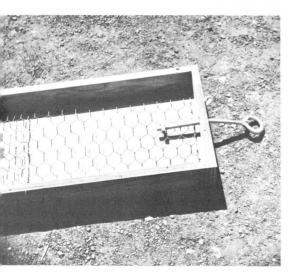

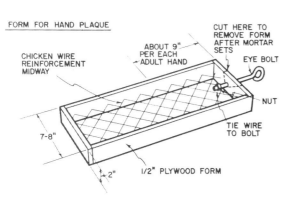

FORM FOR HAND PLAQUE

CHICKEN WIRE REINFORCEMENT MIDWAY

ABOUT 9" PER EACH ADULT HAND

CUT HERE TO REMOVE FORM AFTER MORTAR SETS

EYE BOLT

NUT

TIE WIRE TO BOLT

7-8"

2"

1/2" PLYWOOD FORM

Always a conversation piece, concrete sculpture is set off (or sets off) a plant, as shown in photo here.

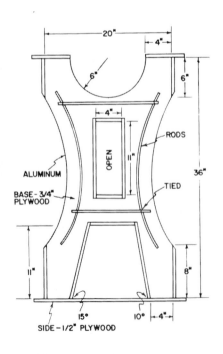

Curved parts of form are made from thin aluminum sheet. Use small box nails to attach to base. When the concrete has set, the aluminum is very easily pulled away.

The inner form does not have to be attached to the base. Hold it in position while you put in the first few trowelfuls of concrete, as shown here.

After castings have been removed from the forms, keep them in a very shady spot (as shown here) for at least a week. Wet down castings every day.

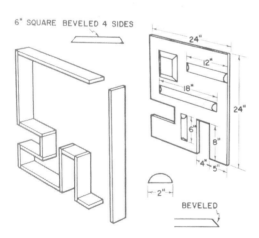

6" SQUARE BEVELED 4 SIDES

24"

12"

18"

24"

6"

8"

4" 5"

2"

BEVELED

Indentations, even fancy faceted effects, are easily accomplished with wood blocks. Just be sure no piece is undercut so that it can't be removed easily.

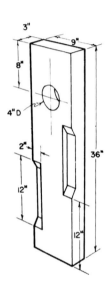

In this piece of concrete sculpture, black, smoothly-polished stones were placed in the form before the mortar mix was poured. The round opening was made by pouring around empty one-pound coffee can.

Bowls

Bowls are not difficult to make if you'll settle for something that doesn't look as though its been turned on a lathe. Actually, a rough, hand-hewn look can have more charm than the finest finish.

The easiest way to make a bowl is to use wet sand as a form. Make a profile template to the shape of the bowl desired and rotate it in the sand pile to form the depression for the bowl. Next step is to trowel in the cement and work it to the shape of the bowl and to an even thickness. Large bowls should have wire mesh reinforcement preshaped before it is put in place. Since the mesh is very flexible this is not difficult to do.

Special steel molds which can be used over and over again are available for bowls. These consist of two shells and a system of clamps which hold them together. Wire mesh can be preshaped by tapping with a mallet in the outer shell. The first pour is worked roughly to the shape of the outer bowl. Then the mesh is put in place and covered with more mix. Then the inner shell is put in place and weighted.

The clamps are then tightened to press the two shells together and produce a smooth bowl of even thickness.

The steel forms (woks, as they are sometimes called) may cost between $30 and $40 but if you plan to cast numerous bowls for yourself or for sale, it might be a good investment.

MOULD OF DAMP SAND
ON FLAT, LEVEL
SURFACE

TEMPLATE

TEMPLATE

PIVOT

DAMP SAND

Concrete bowls are easily cast in forms shaped by templates in damp sand. Pretty with shallow-root plants, the bowls are also effective if half-filled with colored stones or pebbles, and then with water.

These are professionally-made bowls. Don't attempt projects like these until you are very proficient.

A poured concrete wall breaks up a large slab area, provides a puttering place for flower lover.

Concrete-top patio bench has pipe legs threaded into pipe flanges which are bolted to the slab. Legs can be painted black for wrought-iron effect.

Sand-filled ash tray will invite guests to help keep the patio free of crushed-out cigaret butts. Diagram shown below gives details for construction.

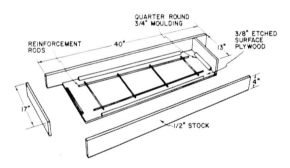

CONCRETE-TOP PATIO BENCH

QUARTER ROUND 3/4" MOULDING
REINFORCEMENT RODS
40"
3/8" ETCHED SURFACE PLYWOOD
13"
4"
17"
1/2" STOCK

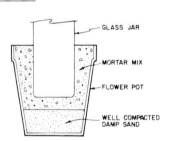

SECTION THRU FORM FOR PATIO ASH TRAY

GLASS JAR
MORTAR MIX
FLOWER POT
WELL COMPACTED DAMP SAND

Patio Bench

We used an etched plywood as the base for the bench-top form, giving the surface of the bench a deeply grooved wood grain finish. Use a regular concrete mix with steel reinforcement rods placed as shown. Apply plenty of oil on the etched plywood if you really wish to pick up detail.

The pipe flanges act as templates when imbedding the bolts in the concrete. If you wish, wood legs can be used by making an under-structure as for patio table.

Ash Tray

You can make these ash trays with a regular mortar mix, a flower pot and a glass jar, as suggested in the drawing. Both the glass jar and the flower pot should be soaked with oil and removed just as soon as the mortar has a chance to set sufficiently. If you want to decorate the rim of the tray, press in brightly colored pebbles before the mortar sets. Fill the ash tray with sand and set it out for use. You'll find it very handsome.

A baking pan was used as the form for this table-top dish garden. Stones were mortared together, given several coats of varnish after they had dried.

Small stones were laid like brick on a plate that served as a base until the project had set. Bottoms of these planters should be covered with felt, etc.

Photo here shows all the ingredients you need to make attractive dish-garden containers. Sand is very fine; asphaltum waterproofs insides.

Table Top Dish Gardens

By using a mortar mix and clean beach stones you can make interesting little planters that will serve indoors as well as out. Suitable containers for use as forms are: baking tins (any shape), heavy cardboard boxes, old dishes, etc.

Here, you don't pour; you build up after forming a solid base. Imbed a line of stones on the perimeter of the form and then raise the sides by adding mortar and imbedding more stones—as you would in building a wall or laying brick in place.

The planters can be waterproofed by coating the insides with liquid asphaltum. If they are to be used indoors on a table or other piece of furniture be sure to cover the bottoms with felt.

Don't be too impatient when casting concrete projects. Let them sit in the forms for at least two days. Then remove the form carefully and set the project in the shade for at least one week so it can cure. •

Tiles

They're long-lasting, add distinction to patios, paths, barbecues, swimming pools

THE word "tile" suggests something luxurious, long lasting and distinctive, and that comes pretty close to describing this material which more and more home owners are discovering for outdoor use. And why not ceramic tile on a patio or in a garden? When you consider its qualifications for a patio floor, a path, a barbecue top or a reflecting pool, tile begins to make good sense.

For one thing it has long lasting color,

an integral part of the material itself. It weathers almost without change. Ceramic tiles are available with texture or smooth enough for patio dancing. Kids can roller skate across a tile patio without scratching it and, of course, it's fireproof. That stray lump of charcoal won't affect it at all. It's easy to clean and except for extreme conditions your garden hose will wash it sparkling new.

There are three basic tile products:

A patio of quarry tile pavers blend harmoniously with brick in the barbecue and planter, as shown in photo above. Tile requires minimum of maintenance, stands up under rugged use, yet is smooth enough for outdoor dancing.

This path from sidewalk to house entrance uses 6x6-inch and 6x9-inch tiles. Note that entry step is in matching tile. The right choice of tile and proper installation result in a very durable, very attractive project, as is indicated here.

PATIO TILE SIZES

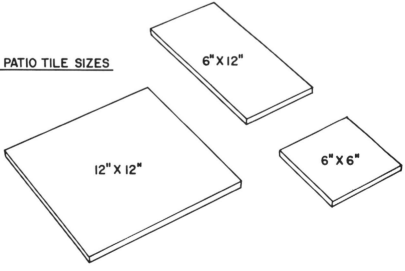

6" X 12"

12" X 12"

6" X 6"

Patio tile blends beautifully with other outdoor materials, is easy to maintain. Photos that follow show construction methods.

First step is to excavate to a three-inch depth below the top surface of what will be the finished patio. Then the entire area should be finished off to a reasonable smoothness, level, and well tamped. This depth of excavation allows for two inches of sand, and for the tile's ⅞-inch thickness.

Form boards should be 1x3 inches and should be installed around the area to be tiled. Drive stakes in about three feet apart and nail the form boards to these level with the tops of the stakes. Then tap down on the stakes until all the form boards are at the desired level and ¾ inch below the desired surface level of the new patio.

SQUARE BOND

BRICK BOND

6X12 BLOCKS

Shovel dry sand into the entire area and to the level of the form boards, as shown in photo here. As an example of how much sand you will need for project, figure that one hundred square feet to that depth will require 17 cubic feet of dry sand.

Shovel the sand around until the entire area is filled level with the form boards or just a bit higher. Then screed it like you would wet concrete to achieve exact levelness. Strikeboard sits on the forms as you slide it forward in a zigzag motion.

Distribute two sacks of dry cement as evenly as possible over each 100 square feet of surface area. Don't throw it by the shovelful, instead let the cement fall from the shovel as you walk around. Another way would be to dump shovelfuls here and there and then spread it evenly with a rake.

Use a rake to thoroughly mix the sand and the cement, but be careful not to dig deep enough to disturb the soil beneath the sand. Spend enough time on this phase of the operation to assure adequate mixing of sand and cement, and be sure to work along the form boards and in all corners. Then use the strikeboard again to screed mixture level with forms.

quarry tile; ceramic mosaic; glazed wall tile. All of them can be used outdoors under certain conditions.

QUARRY TILE is commonly used for heavy duty floors and is an ideal patio paving material regardless of location or climate. Most quarry tiles are either $\frac{1}{2}$ inch or $\frac{3}{4}$ inch thick and range in size from $2\frac{3}{4}$-inch square to 9-inch square. 6x6 inches is the most popular size. You can choose from a color range that includes reds, tans, grays and greens.

CERAMIC MOSAIC TILE can be purchased either glazed or unglazed, although the unglazed is most popular for patio or garden projects. Generally, these are small modular tiles which are available in a wide range of shapes, sizes and colors. Although the finished project usually gives the impression that each small tile has been individually set, they are commonly pasted to a paper backing or "webbing" and are installed in panels that measure 12x12 inches.

SQUARE BOND

BRICK BOND
W/ 6X6 – 12X12 TILES

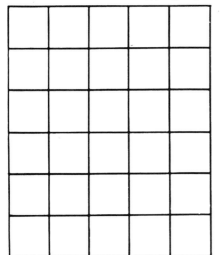

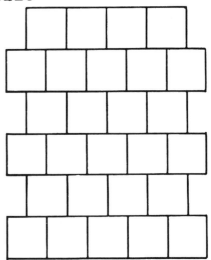

Joints between tiles are filled with grout, made by mixing three parts of sand to one part cement. Mix sand and cement thoroughly, and add water as you keep mixing until the mix can be poured like pancake batter. Then use it to fill the joints, as shown. It's a good idea to keep stirring grout to prevent coarse sand from settling. Tamp in and let the joints set for about fifteen minutes.

You can get a smooth level joint by removing the excess grout and smoothing the joint with a trowel. A slightly concave joint can be achieved by using a round bar. Or you can bend up a length of electrical conduit or copper pipe as shown in photo. Dip the object in water as you work to get smooth surface.

NUMBER OF PATIO TILES REQUIRED
PER 10 SQUARE FEET
(in various patterns)

SQUARE BOND
    9.4 pcs. 12" x 12" tile
    or 40 pcs. 6" x 6" tile
    or 19 pcs. 6" x 12" tile

BRICK BOND
    9.4 pcs. 12" x 12" tile
    or 40 pcs. 6" x 6" tile
    or 19 pcs. 6" x 12" tile

SQUARE PATTERN BOND
    4.9 pcs. 12" x 12" tile
    plus 8.4 pcs. 6" x 12" tile
    plus 3.6 pcs. 6" x 6" tile

DIAGONAL PATTERN BOND
    7.2 pcs. 12" x 12" tile
    plus 8 pcs. 6" x 6" tile
    plus 4 pcs. 6" x 12" tile each lin.
        foot of border

RANDOM BLOCK BOND
    4 pcs. 12" x 12" tile
    plus 8 pcs. 6" x 12" tile
    plus 4 pcs. 6" x 6" tile

HERRINGBONE BOND
    19 pcs. 6" x 12" tile
    plus 4 pcs. 6" x 6" tile each lin.
        foot of border.

Use trowel carefully to remove excess grout, or grout which has been forced from joint by tooling.

SQUARE PATTERN BOND
12X12-6X12-6X6 TILES

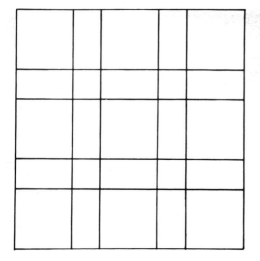

RANDOM BLOCK BOND
(FULL PATTERN SHOWN)
USING 12X12-6X6-6X12 TILES

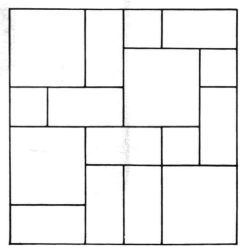

Wait long enough for grout to set so it's not smeary, then clean off the tile with piece of dry burlap.

Wash off the tiles with clean soft rags and clear water to remove cement smears. Stubborn cement is removed with a solution of one part muriatic acid to 20 parts water. Rinse with clear water.

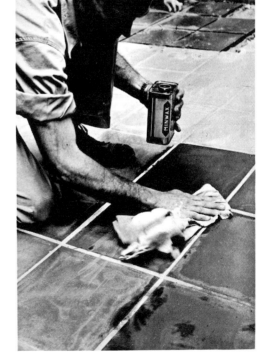

Wait for the tile to dry thoroughly, then apply one or two coats of colorless sealer, as shown here. A good sealer is made by mixing one part boiled linseed oil and four parts paint thinner. Wipe off the excess just before the sealer becomes dry.

Steps

Of vital importance is the relationship between the riser and the tread

STEPS are a means of getting from one level to another without having to pole-vault or climb a rope. Indoors, where space is usually limited, the job is accomplished by placing the stairway in as little space as possible consistent with safe climbing. The shortest distance between two points (in this case a vertical line from one level to the other) doesn't hold with stairs except for the fireman who slides down a pole.

Regardless of the slope between the two levels, a good job can be done with steps only if the relationship between rise (how high you step) and tread (what you step on) is given thorough consideration. Out-

doors, fortunately, you're seldom limited by space, so you can decrease the slope of the stairs to get a good rise and tread relationship even if it does take more room. Steps of this type will also add to appearance. High, steep steps aren't pretty and look almost challenging, while low, broad steps are graceful, inviting—and much safer.

Of course the materials you use can have a bearing on dimensions but for practical purposes, it's recommended by people who have made a study of it, that the nearly ideal relationship between riser and tread on outdoor steps is about six inches for the riser and about 15 inches

Steps at entrance areas should be broad, inviting to guests, establish a feeling of spaciousness, freedom.

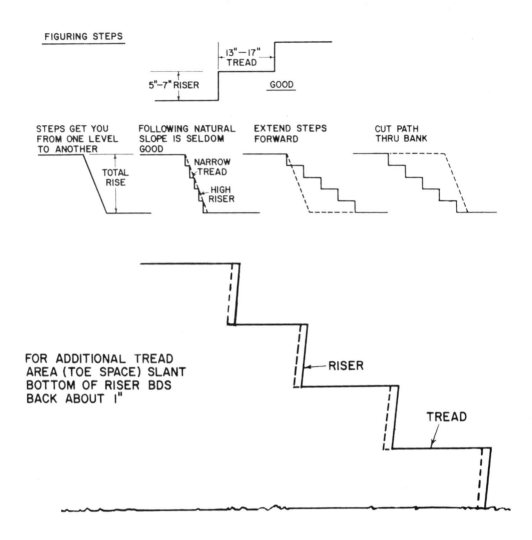

FIGURING STEPS

13"—17" TREAD

5"—7" RISER

GOOD

STEPS GET YOU FROM ONE LEVEL TO ANOTHER

TOTAL RISE

FOLLOWING NATURAL SLOPE IS SELDOM GOOD

NARROW TREAD

HIGH RISER

EXTEND STEPS FORWARD

CUT PATH THRU BANK

FOR ADDITIONAL TREAD AREA (TOE SPACE) SLANT BOTTOM OF RISER BDS BACK ABOUT 1"

RISER

TREAD

BRICK STEPS LAID IN MORTAR OVER POURED CONCRETE BASE

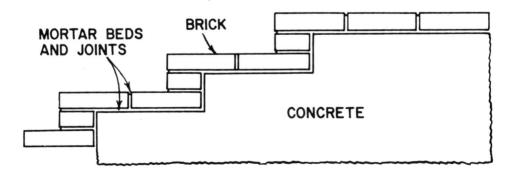

MORTAR BEDS AND JOINTS

BRICK

CONCRETE

CONCRETE BLOCK TECHNIQUE

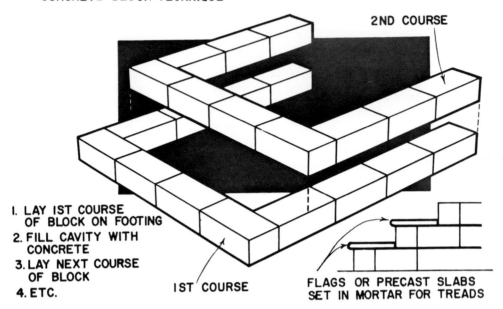

2ND COURSE

1. LAY IST COURSE OF BLOCK ON FOOTING
2. FILL CAVITY WITH CONCRETE
3. LAY NEXT COURSE OF BLOCK
4. ETC.

IST COURSE

FLAGS OR PRECAST SLABS SET IN MORTAR FOR TREADS

for the tread. Generally speaking, the shorter the rise the wider the tread. If you step high, you tend to bring your foot down vertically. If you step low you take more of a walking stride and need more tread. Limits in riser-tread relationship can arbitrarily be established along these lines:

A 3"-4" minimum rise with an 18"-24" tread.

A 7"-8" maximum rise with an 11"-12" tread.

The first represents the gentlest kind of rising steps. The second is as much of a slant upward as is practical and convenient. There are many other combinations in between so you have a great deal of flexibility in designing steps to meet your own particular needs.

Space for steps might be limited in some outdoor locations as between an existing patio and walk, for example. You have to do the best you can with space available, but remember that steps don't always have to go in a straight line. They can turn, break midway at a landing and so forth.

Best way to design steps is to determine the distance (vertically) between the two levels. Then decide on (or determine, if space is limited) the horizontal distance between the top and bottom step. The number of treads multiplied by the width of one tread equals the horizontal distance; the height of one riser multiplied

by the number of risers equals the vertical distance.

When deciding the width of treads, bear in mind that it shouldn't be necessary to take one and a half steps to get to the next level—half steps should never be necessary. If the tread is going to be very wide, let it be either so wide that you take *two* steps on it or just wide enough so *one* step will take you comfortably to the next level without having to stretch or shorten stride.

The width of a stairway is figured on the same basis as the width of a walk. About four feet is an average size, but if you want two people to walk abreast, go to five feet. Figure two feet as a bare minimum and use it only if dictated by circumstances.

A carpenter's square can be used to lay out the triangular cuts in the stringers of wooden steps if you express the rise in feet and fractions of a foot (example:—$2\frac{1}{3}$ feet instead of 2' 4"). When you use the square you use dimensions (and fractions thereof) as inches and fractions of inches. Working on the surface of the stringer so both blades of the square overhang an edge, set the square so the selected inch and its fraction mates with the edge. The rise is represented by the tongue of the square; the run, by the blade. The amount of the square resting on the stringer represents a triangle which you mark off with a pencil. Merely repeat this

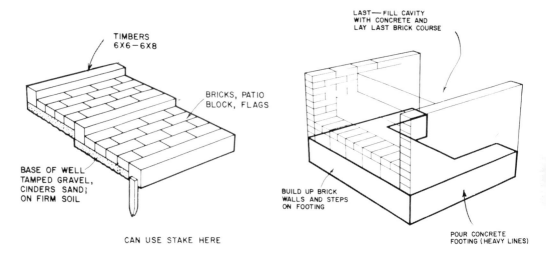

SIMPLE, GRACEFUL STEPS
COMBINING DIFFERENT
MATERIALS

ANOTHER WAY TO FORM BRICK STEPS

TIMBERS
6X6—6X8

BRICKS, PATIO
BLOCK, FLAGS

BASE OF WELL
TAMPED GRAVEL,
CINDERS SAND,
ON FIRM SOIL

CAN USE STAKE HERE

LAST—FILL CAVITY
WITH CONCRETE AND
LAY LAST BRICK COURSE

BUILD UP BRICK
WALLS AND STEPS
ON FOOTING

POUR CONCRETE
FOOTING (HEAVY LINES)

Wood forms for poured concrete steps are very simple to construct. On a steep slope like this, rise should be gentle with broad treads. Center brace will keep concrete from bulging out wide span of riser boards.

Forms for single steps can be constructed before the slab pour, then steps can be poured at same time.

along the stringer until you have marked off enough triangles to equal the total rise. Don't attempt to picture this merely by reading the copy. It's a lot easier to actually do it than read about it. Once you've got the stringer laid out and cut, use it as a template for its mate or for others if the total width of the stairway makes more than two stringers necessary.

A six-foot span of two-inch planks can be supported by two stringers. The treads (the planks you use as steps) can rest on and be nailed right to the cutouts in the stringers. You could accomplish the same thing without having to make the triangular cuts in the stringers by using cleats for the treads to rest on.

Poured Concrete

The simplest kind of forms can be erected to make poured concrete steps, but they must be well braced and rigid. How much bracing depends on step size. If the steps are more than four feet wide it's a good idea to brace or support down the center of the step-forms so that the weight of the concrete won't bulge out the wood. A fairly stiff mixture of concrete should be used and poured in layers. The first layer is poured to the height of the first step, the second layer (after a 30-minute wait) to the second step, and so on. Giving the layers a chance to set awhile prevents top pressure from bumping out the lower steps.

To save on concrete, many builders will use rubble to help fill in the forms. This is

okay so long as you don't overdo it; confine the foreign matter only to the center of the pour. Broken brick, clean stones, etc., can be used. Work the concrete in place with a flat-bladed shovel, especially against the sides of the form. Let the forms remain in place until the concrete has thoroughly set—unless you want to work on the exposed surfaces to get a washed or exposed aggregate finish. Of course, on the treads, you can accomplish this without removing the forms since on poured concrete steps these are exposed even with the form in place.

A slick, steel-troweled finish on concrete steps is seldom a good idea. A wood float will provide a bite for leather soles and increase safety.

Poured concrete can also serve as the base for other materials. If you poured the concrete in the manner described above but did not finish the exposed surfaces, you would still have cast concrete steps, and on this base you could lay brick, flagstone, precast concrete blocks, etc. It would be a matter then of laying down a mortar bed and placing the finishing materials on it. In this case, you'd have to calculate pretty carefully when making the form, taking into consideration the dimensions of the masonry units to be added.

Brick Steps

Brick steps might take a little more time than poured concrete but they certainly aren't more difficult to do. Methods that can be used are flexible. You can pour a

Used brick is a natural-looking material for steps. These steps are solid brick, placed in three tiers.

Poured concrete was used for these steps. Here, risers and treads were veneered with flagstone.

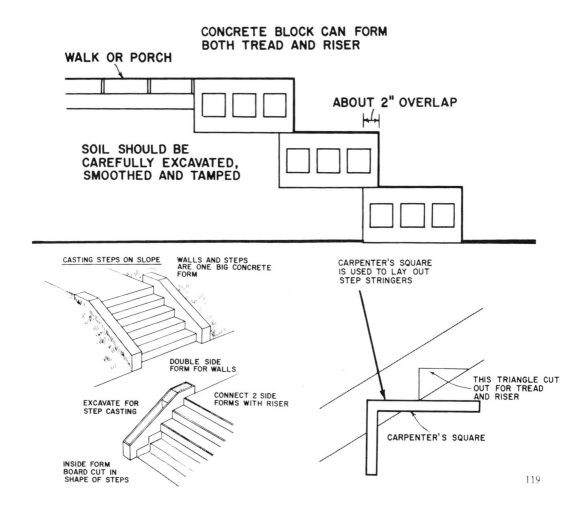

CONCRETE BLOCK CAN FORM
BOTH TREAD AND RISER

WALK OR PORCH

ABOUT 2" OVERLAP

SOIL SHOULD BE
CAREFULLY EXCAVATED,
SMOOTHED AND TAMPED

CASTING STEPS ON SLOPE

WALLS AND STEPS
ARE ONE BIG CONCRETE
FORM

DOUBLE SIDE
FORM FOR WALLS

EXCAVATE FOR
STEP CASTING

CONNECT 2 SIDE
FORMS WITH RISER

INSIDE FORM
BOARD CUT IN
SHAPE OF STEPS

CARPENTER'S SQUARE
IS USED TO LAY OUT
STEP STRINGERS

THIS TRIANGLE CUT
OUT FOR TREAD
AND RISER

CARPENTER'S SQUARE

119

concrete base for the entire step area or you can pour a footing for the outlaying brick. On the first you build up a solid brick structure, stepping back as you go to form risers and treads. On the latter you start by laying what is actually a very low brick wall. Then you fill the cavity with rubble and concrete. Then another brick wall and so on. Since bricks are easily handled, you can go through a "dry run" to see how it will look and to check whether brick dimensions are applicable to your plan.

The brick-laying techniques are the same as if you were doing veneering or building a wall. If the treads are very wide you can lay the brick down in some of the patterns described for walks and patios.

Other Materials

The nice part about working outdoors is that you're less limited. The challenge of blending structural elements into the landscape, making them compatible to nature itself, permits great scope. Poured con-crete and brick are fine but many other materials are good and might be even more appropriate.

Big railroad ties, wood rounds and blocks, loose aggregates, concrete block, tile, timbers, cut stone and field stone—all of these can be used, alone or combined with others. Even logs, used as risers, with well-tamped earth between, can be practical and effective.

Often you can make the stringers and risers out of heavy wood and the treads from another material. The stringers and risers are nailed securely together and set in place. If any excavating is needed limit it to just making room for the frame. With the subassembly in place remove just enough earth in the tread area to make room for the material you will use there. If using brick, dig deep enough for a three-inch layer of sand plus the thickness of the brick. With poured concrete, dig out so you can get a three- or four-inch thickness. You could use loose aggregates here, flags, patio blocks or even plant grass. •

Single step is low with broad tread. Low concrete slab is poured first, then flags laid in bed of mortar.

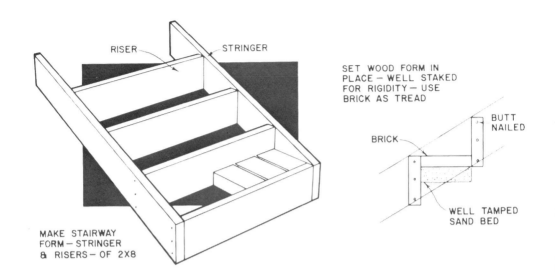

RISER STRINGER

SET WOOD FORM IN
PLACE — WELL STAKED
FOR RIGIDITY — USE
BRICK AS TREAD

BUTT
NAILED

BRICK

WELL TAMPED
SAND BED

MAKE STAIRWAY
FORM — STRINGER
& RISERS — OF 2X8

SIMPLEST KIND OF FORM FOR POURED CONCRETE STEPS

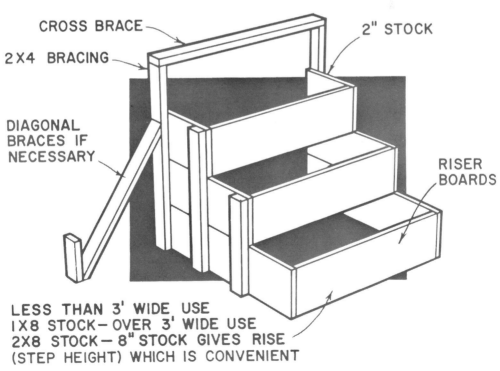

CROSS BRACE

2X4 BRACING

2" STOCK

DIAGONAL
BRACES IF
NECESSARY

RISER
BOARDS

LESS THAN 3' WIDE USE
1X8 STOCK — OVER 3' WIDE USE
2X8 STOCK — 8" STOCK GIVES RISE
(STEP HEIGHT) WHICH IS CONVENIENT

In brick or concrete block, repointing is started by carefully cleaning out joint where the crack appears.

Maintenance

Here are some handy hints on repairing concrete and brickwork

THE most common fault in concrete and masonry work is a crack in a concrete slab or along the joints in brickwork or concrete block. In brickwork these cracks often occur at door and window openings and may be caused by settling of the house foundation and/or moisture in the mortar, which expands when frozen to spread the joint and form a crack. Uneven settling and extremes in temperature can do the same thing to a concrete slab. A job done well

from the beginning can minimize these faults but they appear in even the most professional work. Repair, however, is simple and consists mainly of opening up the crack, cleaning it and filling it again.

In brickwork, dig out all the crumbling, loose, dried out mortar from the joint. You can do this with a small cold chisel, working slowly so as to avoid cracking the brick. It isn't necessary to go deeper than one inch but it is important to get out all the old mortar and to try to clean the joint to the surface of the brick. A thin layer of old mortar that might cling to the brick won't be harmful so long as the bond is firm.

Use a small brush, that will fit between the brick, to clean out the joint and remove all dust. Spray the crack, inside and out, and the adjacent areas with a fine spray from a garden hose or use a brush to do the job. But be sure the area is *wet*. A good method is to do the wetting operations several times about 15 minutes apart. This will give the porous brick a chance to absorb the water. A dry area would suck all the moisture out of the new mortar and cause a weak repair job.

With the crack prepared make a mortar mix of one part portland cement, one part lime and six parts mortar sand—or you can buy ready mixed *pointing* mortar. Add enough water so the mix can be pushed easily into the crack. When ready, shove as much of the mortar into the crack as you can with a trowel, then use a piece of wood to ram the mortar in solidly. Tap the wood (thickness of wood should equal thickness of mortar joint) gently with a hammer. When the joint won't take any more mortar, let it set for a while and then tool the joint to match surrounding areas.

Repointing joints in a concrete block wall is essentially the same. Be very careful when deepening and cleaning out the crack that you don't chip off adjacent units.

Cracks in concrete sidewalks or slabs should be widened enough to remove all loose concrete. Work with a hammer and chisel, chipping off pieces at the edge of the crack and working back to widen it. To start off, angle the chisel toward the crack, then undercut the opening by tilting the chisel in the opposite direction. Don't worry about doing the job in a perfectly uniform manner or in a straight line; the most important part of the job is the key which you form by undercutting and the removal of all damaged material.

Clean out all loose sand, stones and chips from the repair area and wet it and adjacent areas thoroughly with a garden hose.

A good cement mortar can be mixed using one part of cement to three of sand, or you can purchase ready mixed concrete patching material in large sacks. Actually this is probably the best way to do it since you can always keep some on hand for use when needed.

Apply the mix to the wet crack with a trowel, packing it in solidly and slightly higher than surrounding areas. Use a small piece of wood as a strikeboard to level the patch, then finish it to match. Do a good curing job by covering the area with newspaper or burlap and keep the covering wet for several days.

When the opening is prepared and has been cleaned out, wet it, adjacent areas thoroughly.

Plug opening solidly with fresh mortar. Trowel it flush; after it sets, tool it to match other joints.

123

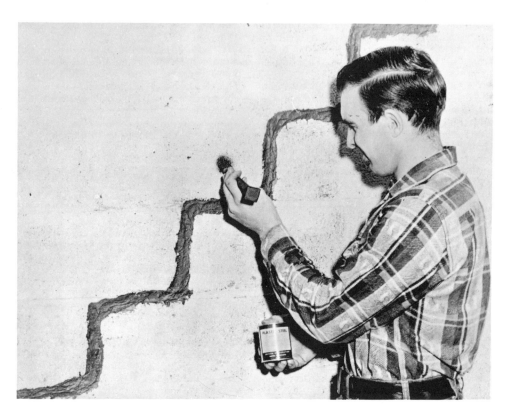

Plastic steel, bought in can, can be used to repair masonry work or to anchor bolts, as shown in photo.

Plastic steel is also good for anchoring wood to masonry structure, as photograph below shows.

Plastic steel is also used for sealing opening around pipes, other objects passing through walls.

Sometimes repair work becomes necessary right after the forms have been removed from a fresh pour, as above. It's good idea to oil boards (riser boards, here) so they won't pull away concrete when removed.

If concrete does pull away with the form boards, place new concrete immediately before the fresh pour has a chance to set too much.

Water used for cement paint should be fit enough to drink. A shallow mixing pan makes it easy to avoid settling of materials.

Measure water and paint powder carefully. Read instructions on container and follow the manufacturer's directions to the letter.

Mix materials thoroughly until they reach consistency of thick, rich cream. Worker in the photograph is using a hand eggbeater.

Use a "fog" spray to dampen, not soak, the wall evenly and thoroughly, as shown in the photograph above. Apply the paint while the wall is damp and after all the surface water has disappeared from view.

Apply the paint with a stiff, bristle brush, as shown in photograph below. Brushes sold for applying whitewash, or ordinary paint brushes aren't strong enough to force cement paint into pores of masonry.

Scrub-paint mortar joints first. Time the job so you are applying the paint while the wall is in the shade. This keeps the paint from drying too fast.

After joints are covered, go over the entire wall. Scrub enough to fill the pores. Keep first coat damp for about 12 hours before putting on second coat.

Start "fog-spray cure" as soon as the paint has hardened sufficiently to prevent damage. Continue applications to keep the wall damp for 24 hours.

Elastic caulking compound that won't crack, loosen or dry out gives watertight seal around windows. Comes in cartridge form, or bulk for putty knife.

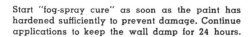

Caulking compound has very good weathering and adhesive qualities, so use it to seal joints between flashing and masonry, joints in concrete, etc.

Caulking compound available in tubes, too. Has a roll-up key that squeezes the compound out the nozzle in a fine stream, makes for easy handling.

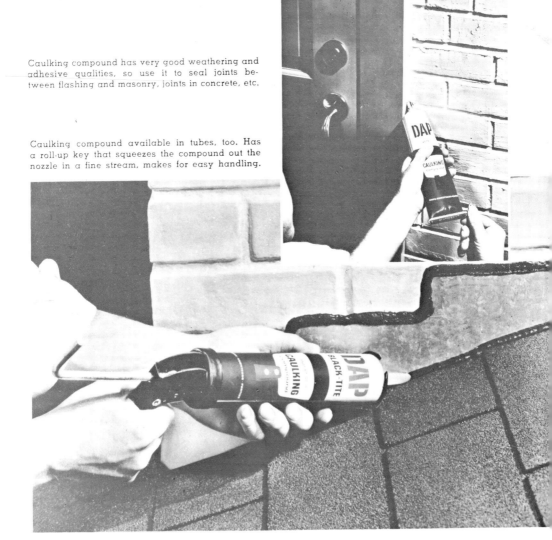

Concrete masonry walls can be prettied up and maintained by painting them with a portland cement base paint. You can buy the special cement paint in a dry state to be mixed with water before application. The dry material includes waterproofing agents, coloring agents, etc., so the application of cement protects as well as beautifies.

The surface to which the cement paint is applied should be clean—oil, dirt, soil, any substance which could prevent the paint from adhering should be removed. It's also a good idea to check the wall thoroughly for cracks and other imperfections and to repair these before going further. Spray the wall with a garden hose first. Be sure it is uniformly damp but not soaked. Prepare the paint by adding the amount of water recommended by the manufacturer and be sure that it is thoroughly mixed and that you mix frequently during application to avoid settling. One trick the professionals use is to keep the paint in a shallow container. Then they do some slight mixing each time they dip the brush.

A stiff bristle brush is best for application and this is more a scrubbing job than it is a "painting" job. Exterior concrete walls should be given two coats. Interior walls, unless weatherproofing is a factor can be finished with one coat.

A cement base paint should be properly cured for it to be most effective. This is just a question of keeping it moist with a fine spray so that wind, heat or sunshine won't dry it out too quickly. Keep the first coat moist for at least 12 hours, the second coat for about 48. •

Waterproofing

New products decorate as they protect interior walls against moisture

SPECIAL products are available which effectively control passage of moisture through inherently porous masonry walls. When used correctly they do the job either above or below grade and decorate as they protect—a good point when remodeling a below-grade basement into a playroom or den. DURA-STOP, DURA-DRI and CE-MENTICO are trade names for products each designed to do a specific job. Used together they do the job of waterproofing from scratch to finish. DURA-STOP is actually a "hydraulic" cement that has a very fast setting time (three to five minutes). Mixed according to directions it becomes a paste that resembles putty. It's used to fill cracks that are first prepared by chiseling them wider than they were

Clean the wall carefully. Back of garden rake is effective when brushing won't do the job. Chisel out points where water penetration is really evident. All cracks are opened to a ¼-inch width.

All structural cracks (caused by normal house-settling motion) should be treated similarly. Loose mortar can be scraped from wall with a stiff wire brush. Check all points for water seepage.

originally (to about a quarter of an inch). This material can actually be used to dam water that is flowing through a crack under pressure. The way to do this is to hold the mixed compound until it feels warm. Then jam it into the crack or hole and hold it in place for about five minutes. Excess material is brushed smooth before set-time is complete.

The second material (DURA-DRI) is a protective coating that controls moisture penetration through porous substances. It can be used on concrete block, brick, stucco, poured concrete, etc. It is applied either by brush or trowel in an amount relative to the amount of water penetration evident or expected. When the material is troweled on it is good practice to precede and follow the troweling with a brushed-on application.

CEMENTICO is a water-repellent cement paint for all masonry surfaces that can be applied by brush or spray gun. It's available in half a dozen or so basic colors that can be intermixed to provide others.

When redoing a wall, follow this procedure. Remove all loose mortar from the wall by scraping it with a stiff wire brush. The back of a garden rake is an effective tool to use when brushing alone won't do. Check all points on the wall, especially at the floor and wall joint and along the joints of the lower courses, for excessive water seepage. If you find points where water might actually be entering in small streams, chisel these points or joints open

Jam all cracks full of the compound and smooth off surface of the fills with water and fiber brush. The next step: prime the filled and patched areas.

The entire wall must be uniformly saturated with water. Check this by looking for spotty drying. When spraying use fine spray from garden hose.

wide enough to relieve the pressure. Form small holes if necessary and widen existing cracks to a ¼″ width. If water seems to be entering at the angle between floor and wall, chisel an opening at that point.

Cracks which were caused by normal settling of the house should be treated in a similar manner. Use a chisel to widen the cracks whether they are along a joint or across the face of any units.

Next step is to clean out openings and fill with the cement compound. Form the mixed material into a lump about the size of an egg and start to fill the cracks working from the top of the wall to the bottom. Don't mix too much of the compound at one time. If it becomes crumbly during use, discard it and mix another batch.

After the cracks are filled and the compound has set, use a fiber brush and water to work over the filled surfaces and level them off. Patched areas and filled cracks should be primed with the protective coating previously described.

Before going further the whole wall must be soaked with water. It's important for the entire wall surface to absorb an equal amount of water. Check this by looking for spotty drying—a good indication that the area requires more water. The water is

best applied to the wall with a fine spray from a garden hose. As soon as the surface water on the wall has disappeared, apply the protective coating. So that the bottom of the wall will have extra protection, apply the coating to the bottom quarter of the wall first. Then shift to the top of the wall and work down putting a second application over the bottom area.

The surface should be kept moist for about 12 hours after which a second coat is applied starting at the top of the wall and working down—or the original procedure can be followed for even more protection at the base of the wall. After about six hours, spray the wall with a garden hose and repeat this two or three times daily for the next few days.

While this technique will effectively seal an inside wall, it might be a good idea if excessive water is present to examine the foundation line on the outside of the house. One way to help keep a basement dry is to minimize water collection against the wall. Dig a trench down to the base of the foundation and waterproof the wall on the outside. Fill the bottom of the trench with gravel and lay a drain line to run off the water. Top the line with more gravel and then back fill. •

When surface water on wall disappears, apply protective coating. Start the coating at base of wall, shift to top and work down, recoating lower part.

Touch up thin or missed areas and keep the surface moist for about 12 hours, after which a second coat is applied starting at top and working down.

Building

The formidable quality of a high brick wall is eased by openings left in the structure, as shown in the photograph above. Tall vine-like plants, growing in a planting strip on the other side of the wall, are pulled through the openings so that they relieve wall on both sides.

A carport wall of split block construction adds warmth and elegance to any yard. Split block is a variety of new-type concrete masonry, and despite its luxurious and ultra-modern appearance, its "in-place" cost can be less than face brick. The lattice-work pattern lets air and light in so you can actually use the carport as an outdoor living room when you want to. The planting area is surrounded by solid concrete block as is the gravel-filled section of the driveway.

Ideas

Here are 14 clever items to

build from concrete and brick

Douglas Fir Plywood Assoc.

Title Council of America

Here's a carport-pergola that provides an imaginative solution to the need for a garage, lawn storage area, and patio. Loose gravel is confined by headers that are set flush with the lawn area. This handsome project, which measures 2x20x20x10 feet, can be built for about $300 if you do the work. This includes all materials needed.

The luxury of tile is used to enhance an idea that can mark any home with distinction and good taste. The pool can be a constant enjoyment whether you're relaxing on the patio or sitting in the living room. Quarry tiles and unglazed ceramic mosaics were used. Jobs such as this require very painstaking care for professional results.

Filon Plastics Corp.

Wood and masonry units are nicely combined on the street wall, as shown here. Different types of brick, masonry units, adobe block (natural or painted) can be used.

Note how different materials can blend in together and in a natural outdoor setting: concrete patio, brick walls and walks, wood, plastic cord. The cord provides a feeling of privacy without cutting out the view. The large expanse of the concrete patio is relieved with an occasional diamond pattern, as shown in photo.

Puritan Cordage Mills

Circular niche in this swimming pool was designed with a seat for cool, comfortable relaxing. The table was specially built, has cast aluminum legs and is rimmed by aluminum molding to confine the ceramic tile top, as shown in the photograph above. None of the material used in the table construction can be harmed by water in the pool.

Simple masonry units, arranged in an interesting fashion as shown in photo below, provide interesting, decorative wall. Careful form construction needed for concrete frame.

Little, comparatively simple touches, such as this masonry-unit raised planter bed, can do much to enhance any outdoor living area. A fairly light footing is all you need to set the blocks on edge. Carefully selected plantings with a semiconcealed light will provide special point of interest.

If you plan a big wall, why not incorporate a grill, fire box and counter? The one shown in photo here is the result of careful pre-planning. Flue for the grill can be constructed right in the wall. The counter, which is covered with red, unglazed ceramic tile, is built around steel bars which were imbedded in the wall when it was built.

Title Council of America

139

Confine traffic to a parking area by setting in wood bumper strips. This can be a 4x4-inch beam set on short posts set in the pour, as shown here.

This patio-porch is all poured concrete, and yet see how areas of definition are established through choice of surface treatment. There is a definite separation between the step-out slab and the outdoor room, merely because the concrete in one place was given a flagstone effect through the use of a grooving tool.

A lovely screen is set off by the large "cobblestones" which are simply planted on firm soil. This provides a clean walk area without destroying the beautiful sylvan setting. The screen is made of tempered Masonite panels set in redwood.

Note how use of brick carries indoor living to the outdoors and vice versa. Similar floor material with smooth passageway through wide door, creates feeling of lovely spaciousness.

Masonite Corp.

Filon Plastics Corp.

141

New Epoxy Resins

They play an important role in both concrete repair and installation

THERE is little doubt that the new epoxy adhesives and resins are going to play an important role in the field of concrete and masonry work. Not only in the area of repair but in the initial installation. Epoxies are a brand new item. Although it has been definitely determined that they will be extremely valuable in the field, extensive experimental programs are still being carried out by many organizations to pin-point specific use and feasible procedures.

To point up the value of the new materials consider this. When a concrete surface is damaged beyond ordinary repair and requires a new topping, the correct procedure, if the repair job is to be worthwhile, is to pour a new layer that is at least an inch thick. When epoxies are used, however, the new topping can be

Epoxies must be mixed and used exactly as described by manufacturer. Proper proportions of materials and correct mixing are very important factors, and can, if done correctly, result in the most gratifying manner.